by Fairfield Osborn

OUR PLUNDERED PLANET

THE LIMITS OF THE EARTH

THE LIMITS OF THE EARTH

The LIMITS
of the EARTH

by FAIRFIELD OSBORN

LITTLE, BROWN AND COMPANY
Boston

LIBRARY OF CONGRESS CATALOG CARD NO. 53-7324

FIRST EDITION

Published simultaneously
in Canada by McClelland and Stewart Limited

PRINTED IN THE UNITED STATES OF AMERICA

To all who care about tomorrow

CONTENTS

ix

CONTENTS

THE LIMITS OF THE EARTH

I. THE REACHES OF TIME AND SPACE

The shadows of coming events

W<small>E LIVE</small> in the hour of glory and of fear. The triumphs and tragedies of past ages are being joined as the present century runs its course.

Man is becoming aware of the limits of his earth. The isolation of a nation, or even a tribe, is a condition of an age gone by. No longer is Lhasa a sanctuary — no longer is any community or country immune from the influences and pressures that pervade the entire world. For better or for worse, the people of New York and of Novo Redondo, of Delhi and of Danzig, are linked to a common future. Empires dissolve or struggle to survive in changing form under the impact of forces that are both physical and social. These forces stem from a common cause — the unfilled need of rapidly increasing numbers of people for the essentialities of life.

The fierce and dreadful conflict now dividing the East and the West is more than a clash of ideologies. It is a battle not only for the minds of men but for the resources of the earth — the inadequate resources — the resources of which there are fewer for each person the world over each day. Communism has become the social and political manifestation of need or want. Democracy, mother of individual liberty, flourishes best upon the well-being of people.

The strength of any political system will, in the long run, depend upon its capacity to protect people against conditions of want that are now becoming increasingly intolerable. The answer cannot be found through war, for the problem will still remain. Social and moral points of view, as well as spiritual concepts, are, as ever, profoundly involved.

More than a billion people are in want, hundreds of millions are balanced on the starvation line. They hear and dream of the magic that is freedom or liberty. They are well aware of the material resources that are required to nurture it. The determining question in the future of civilization is whether the supply of resources to be gained from the earth can prove adequate not only to meet the basic needs of people but to support the complex requirements of modern culture and economy. What we call the "free world" has it in its power to find the answer to this primal question. The effort to accomplish this cannot be measured in days or in years but at best in terms of a generation. To succeed, we must clearly understand the facts regarding existing and potential resources. Equally, the facts regarding populations, their growths and pressures, must be recognized and dealt with deliberately and fearlessly. It is needless to try to measure which of these two problems is the more immediate, or the more critical. The destiny of man depends upon the resolving of both.

Sometimes, in faraway moments, our thoughts turn to the meaning of mankind's life on this earth — the millenniums from animalism to the atomic age.

There is no central theme. We cling to the conviction of evolution and progress — and hold before us the radiant grail of intellectual and spiritual growth. Achievements and failures merge and dissolve as we contemplate the hundred or more centuries since a human hand first placed form and color upon the cave walls of Altamira. The writings of history cannot give us the perspective for which we search. The story of human life, though similar through all ages, defies definition in totality. So it is that the historian, conscious of the inscrutable whole, perforce deals with definable parts — with the arts and sciences, with religion and philosophy, with trade and industry, and with the rise or fall of political power.

The purpose of this book is to stress the influence, both as regards past history and the present world situation, exerted by the relationship between people and the resources of the earth. This is indeed the eternal equation — the formula that holds the key to human life, then, now and tomorrow.

When resources have proved adequate not only to meet the basic needs of peoples but also to support their economies, nations and cultures have flourished. The so-called "great periods" of history are intimately identified with this favorable relationship. Lacking it, apparently indestructible empires have dissolved.

The essential components within the total of natural resources available to man are those that are constantly being created and renewed by the vital processes of the earth itself. All of these are derived either from plant life or from animal life, whether of land or marine origin. These, in the full sense of the term, are *living resources,* not only because they themselves are alive, but also because they provide the foods and fibers which sustain man's own life, as well as a substantial part of his industry and economy.

While the great edifice of civilization has been built upon the development and use of a vast number of natural resources that are inanimate and nonreplenishable — a fact clearly evident as man progressed successively from the age of stone to the age of bronze and, finally, to the age of iron — the organic resources obtained from the soils, from the forests and from the sea are those that are of essential importance. They have been the primary factors in man's history in the past, responsible for his food supply and other physical needs as well as of immeasurable influence upon his cultural and social development.

We human beings are suspended in three-dimensional time: the past, the present and the future. We are apt to disregard the first and are quite uncertain about the last. Only of the present are we sure — but are we? A moment ago it was the future and in another it will be the past. In turn, we exist on the face of a small planet, under a dynamic canopy of life-sustaining atmosphere. Permeating the influences and conditions that surround us is distance, the measurer. We need to cast our gaze into the reaches of both time and space — into the past as into far places — for only so can we hope to gain perspective as to *now, here,* and, above all, as to *tomorrow.*

Any exploration into history becomes more revealing if we can discover the causes that led to the decline or disappearance of once great nations. Our interest may center principally upon birth and upon life itself, but all the while the enigma of death is a constant challenge to our curiosity. As in the individual, so in the nation, there is no single cause. The interplay of forces, physical and mental, that controls the destiny of human society is infinitely complex and indeed defies formulization. But there are clues, there are precedents and patterns; and these at least we can contemplate, although a complete understanding of cause and effect may elude us.

The glory that was Greece! What combination of circumstances brought twilight and eventual darkness to that shining period in human history? The well-ordered and stable society of the age of Pericles seemingly contained the quality of permanence. Greece would not crumble, so it appeared, as had its neighbors to the east — those empires of Babylonia and of Assyria. They, too, in their day had the appearance of permanence — their riches accumulated from the fertility of their lands watered by the Tigris and the Euphrates, their peoples lived well, built flourishing cities, established governments, developed the arts and enjoyed a degree of welfare unknown to more primitive peoples. We cannot be sure of the various causes that led to the breakdown of the Near Eastern civilizations. But one fact stands clear — their land lost its productivity and their resources failed them. A cradle of civilization became a desert.

Likewise, centuries later, forces of dissolution were at work in Greece. The following observations tell a story:

> At that period, however, with which we are dealing, when Attica was still intact, what are now her mountains were lofty, soil-clad hills; her so-called shingle plains of the present day were full of rich soil; and her mountains were heavily afforested — a fact of which there are still visible traces. There are mountains in Attica which can now keep nothing but bees, but which were clothed, not so very long ago, with fine trees producing timber suitable for roofing the largest buildings; and roofs hewn from this timber are

still in existence. There were also many lofty cultivated trees, while the country produced boundless
pasture for cattle. The annual supply of rainfall was
not lost, as it is at present, through being allowed to
flow over the denuded surface into the sea, but was
received by the country, in all its abundance, into her
bosom where she stored it in her impervious potter's
earth and so was able to discharge the drainage of the
heights into the hollows in the form of springs and
rivers with an abundant volume and a wide territorial
distribution. The shrines that survive to the present
day on the sites of extinct water supplies are evidence
for the correctness of my present hypothesis.*

This statement was not written by a modern observer.
It was written by Plato and he wrote it over two thousand years ago. He recognized that forests, water supply, and fertile soils were related so intimately that
they were in truth a unity, not independent elements.
Yet his observations have an even deeper significance,
for he sensed that land-illness and a deterioration of
the physical environment would inevitably injure the
continuity of his country's welfare. The dark shadow
of resource failure was traveling westward from Assyria
and the lands to the east. Unquestionably other de-
teriorating factors, not wholly unrelated, were at
work, including the succession of exhausting wars be-

* Toynbee, Arnold J., *Greek Historical Thought* (From Homer
to the Age of Heraclius). J. M. Dent, London, 1924, pp. 169–170.
Translation taken from Plato: *Collected Works,* Oxford Text,
Vol. IV.

tween the Grecian states, as well as suspected but not provable inroads upon the health and strength of the Grecian people from malaria and other epidemics. There were also purely economic causes. For instance, Athens had been assisted in gaining its eminence by the treasures of silver drawn from its mines at Laurium, where exploration has since exposed more than two thousand shafts and a hundred miles of underground workings. This wealth helped to bring the Athenian state to a condition where its culture could flower, and aided its rise to political power by making possible the hiring of mercenaries and the subsidizing of its co-members in the Panhellenic League. The exhaustion of the mines was one of the many factors that led to the decline of Athenian intellectual glory and political leadership.

Other theories endeavor to account for the end of that remarkable period in human history. One is that changes in climate occurred in both Asia Minor and the Mediterranean Basin and that these changes gradually undermined the fertility of the land. While it is true that many regions of the earth are subject to cyclical climatic change, it is highly implausible that those that may have occurred in the Mediterranean region during the centuries of ascendancy and decline of Grecian civilization could, either in character or extent, have had any substantial bearing upon the well-being of its peoples. As a matter of fact, any changes in climate would equally have affected the Italian peninsula, lying only a few hundred miles to the west, whose people were at the dawn of their power.

The widespread deforestation so vividly described by Plato would, in itself, have robbed the country of its dependable water supply, the prime requisite for the stability of its agriculture. The resources of the country, as of those lands to the east upon which it had so long depended, were indeed showing signs of drying up, but the causes were man-made, not natural. One can sense, and yet not positively identify, a contemporaneous deterioration of environment and peoples.

We can reject the implications that lie behind Plato's observations if we will. They provide a clue, but how important a one we shall never know. The shining years were running out, and at the end Greece became just another colony of an emerging and vital force — the Roman Empire.

Now we can commence to see more clearly, to explore more intimately, this relationship between peoples and their resources, for the lives of the Romans stand vividly before us through the writings of their statesmen and philosophers. The mists that shroud so much of the history of earlier peoples are dissolved. The story of Rome, from the days of Camillus to those of Constantine, suspended in high light above the Dark Ages, assumes the character of a prologue to modern times. Assuredly there is an affinity between *then* and *now,* and, in this light, certain of the causes of the Roman Empire's decline may be considered.

The Romans themselves, even in the early days of the empire, became aware of the progressive disintegration of their country. Some expressed the view that *corruptio* was responsible for the constantly increasing troubles facing the empire: corruption in personal morals, graft in government and in the activities of wealthy people, corruption resulting from poverty, indeed an all-pervading decline in ethical standards. We do not know that the senate established any investigating committees, but it did formally complain, and called upon the Emperor Tiberius for action. He sent a message to the senate that read in part:

> That these abuses are the subject of discussion at every table and the topic of conversation in all private circles, I know quite well. And yet, let a law be made with proper sanctions, and the very men who call for a reform will be the first to make objections. The public peace, they will say, is disturbed; illustrious families are in danger of ruin. . . .

Many, however, placed the blame upon the concentration of ownership of land into large estates known as latifundia, which drew from the elder Pliny the remark that "the latifundia were ruining Rome [*Italiam*] as well as its provinces." Seneca, although himself one of the richest landowners, gave public expression to his concern by asking, "How far will you extend the bounds of your possessions? A large tract of land, sufficient heretofore for a whole nation, is scarce wide enough for a single lord." Cicero had earlier reported that the entire commonwealth could not muster two thousand property owners.

The poet Horace describes his reasons for his somber view of things by stating that the earlier great accomplishments of his people were due in large part to the deeds of a sturdy farmer race, now dispossessed by the growth of the latifundia system, demoralized, eking out a bare living on the land or moving to Rome as paupers dependent on government doles.

But was Horace not still dealing with effects rather than causes? For instance, if the large landed estates were at the bottom of the trouble, how did it happen that they came into existence?

There is a pretty clear trail of evidence that indicates that the initial movement to eliminate the small independent landowner, the bulwark of Roman society in the early days of the Republic, took place even as far back as 400 B.C. However, the body blow to Roman agriculture, as well as indeed to Roman society, followed upon the final triumph of the wars with Carthage almost three centuries later. In passing, Sicily, then so productive, was presumably one of the principal causes of the bitter conflict between Rome and Carthage. The great Carthaginian estates, operated by agent farmers and slave labor, became a model for the

Roman patricians, although slave labor never was used in Italy to the degree it had been in Africa. The days when sound and responsible land use was an inherent part of Roman culture were now about over. Annual taxes paid by conquered provinces brought into Italy large supplies of wheat in competition with domestic production. From being tillers of the soil and careful husbandmen, the Romans became, like the Phoenicians before them, the richest merchants in the world.

Columella, in the first century A.D., writes of Latium, once a highly fertile region, as a place where the population would have died of starvation had it not been for imported grain. By Columella's time the arable lands of Italy had declined to a production of less than four bushels for every bushel sown, a ratio so meager that grain farming was generally abandoned. (A present-day wheat farmer in the Midwestern grain belt of the United States would expect a return of at least ten bushels for every bushel sown. Under more intensive agriculture, as practiced in some of the Eastern states or in Europe, a far higher return could be gained.) The final consequence was that Italy had to give up the production of subsistence crops and turn more and more to what we might call "secondary" agriculture, such as vineyards and olive groves. The day was over when Italy had a self-sufficient agriculture. The Roman people were compelled to look to Sicily and their African colonies for their food supply.

The eventual depletion of the land of Italy itself is hard to visualize. For instance, the Theodosian Code, written towards the end of the fourth century A.D., records that the abandoned fields in Campania alone amounted to more than three hundred thousand acres. Through the centuries, from the time of Cato to that of Theodosius, the deterioration of the peoples and lands of the Italian Peninsula infected the empire's provinces, whose lands, one after another, were exploited and depleted. *Agri deserti* — abandoned fields — both at home and abroad, became physical portents of political collapse.

This situation suggests an age-old question. Were the Romans *innately* warlike and power-seeking or were they driven to their wars of conquest in order to insure their own survival? We can only observe that the vineyards on abandoned croplands and the Roman legions were contemporaneous phenomena.

The social consequences of a failing agriculture can be clearly identified. In Rome's case they contributed to the disintegration of the nation.

The unfolding story should not deceive us into thinking that the Romans lacked a sound knowledge of agriculture. Their *Scriptores Rei Rustica* indicate agricultural techniques as competent as any practiced during the Middle Ages or even those of modern Europe a hundred and fifty years ago. This fact carries a powerful moral for us today in dealing with the existing crises of food shortages throughout the world. The obstacle was not one of inadequate knowledge but of the practical difficulties of its sustained and widespread application. In Rome, as in the glowing civilizations that preceded it, the crushing effect of adverse social and economic influences was to reduce the practice of good agriculture and thus to throttle the flow of resources upon which the life of the empire depended. All of this happened a long time ago, and we today may well say, "Ah, but it is altogether different now." Perhaps — but let us consider this question in later pages, as we proceed in our search for better understanding concerning people and their earth-home, and, more specifically, the present world problem of populations and resources.

It is difficult, even with the perspective of twenty centuries, to comprehend the rapidity of the transformation that befell Italy. In her early days she was famous for her wheat, which provided not only her own population but was exported in quantities to Greece. The fertility of the soil of southern Italy, today a desolate land, was presumably the reason for the Greek colonies that had earlier established themselves in that region.

All through these years another form of corrosion was undermining the strength of the Roman people — the breaking up of family life. One may dismiss it as a coincidence, but the fact remains that the social changes that resulted in the gradual depletion of land as a *physical* asset were paralleled by the relinquishment of family life as a *moral* asset.

The reason for the disappearance of family life is not hard to find. In the earlier days the simplicity and severity of Roman character found expression in the home. Marriage was a religious act which made the home a holy place. In it lived Vesta, whose altar was the hearth, together with the spirits of the ancestors, who, in the form of the lares, guarded the house from harm, and, in the form of the penates, blessed the family possessions. The father was the priest of these gods, the owner of the estate and the master of his wife and children. There was no limit to the authority of the father in ancient Rome. Even if the son were a senator or a magistrate, the father could drag him home and punish him for misconduct. Quite an idea! No doubt there are some fathers today who wish this old custom could be revived! Irrespective of the power of the father, the center of family and religion alike was the home and the land around it. When individual ownership of these passed into the big estates, the binding values of family and religion alike were swept away. It seems not unlikely that the founders of the early Roman church, witnessing these tragic changes, re-created the concept of the holiness of marriage as an essential tenet of Christian belief, a continuing essentiality in Roman Catholicism to this day.

As the once great empire approached its eclipse, land

and morals became political issues. Towards the end of the second century A.D., everyone, either in Italy or the provinces, was permitted to take possession of abandoned fields, even if they were the emperor's own property, and whosoever was tilling those fields could become their rightful owner and proprietor.

By the fourth century A.D., the Emperor Constantine found it necessary to issue laws that the state must provide for the children of indigent parents, whether residing in Italy or the African provinces, in order to check the growing practice of selling or pledging children or — hard as it is to believe — deliberately allowing them to starve to death.

The time had passed when these and other desperate efforts to reverse the trend, to restore vigor and purpose to a faltering civilization, could succeed. Rome's hour had struck. As the fifth century was dawning, Alaric and his fierce Goths sacked the queen city that for eight hundred years had seen no enemy in her streets.

It is written that "the sack of Rome astonished mankind, for all had supposed the city inviolable and in her fall they thought they saw the ruin of the law and order of the world." Law and order! They are the framework of human conduct which rests on a foundation that in Rome's case had long since been dissolved. Mankind need not have been so astonished.

The sun of power moved slowly to the west. A thousand years after the fall of Rome it shone for a while upon the people of Spain, upon the last westward peninsula jutting out from the body of Europe.

Few regions on earth have endured such turbulent experiences continued through the sweep of historical time. Once, this bounteously endowed peninsula had been a magnet that drew to it one invasion after another. Stronger and more numerous people had come, drawn by the lure of the country's richness in minerals or by the agricultural fertility of its eastern and southern regions. The tale ran that silver was so plentiful that not only could vessels be filled with it but ships' utensils, including even anchors, could be made of it.

The Carthaginians had come, before the days of Christ, fortifying themselves in their long struggle with Rome. The conquering Romans took the land as their province, accelerating the processes of exploitation. The wealth of the land poured out to benefit the empire. As an evidence of the tempo of mining activity, it is recorded that, in the second century B.C., in Cartagena alone, forty thousand slave miners were chained to their positions in tunnels lighted by earthenware oil lamps and the mercury mines were turned into prisons where condemned slaves were crowded in forced labor.

The forests covering the Pyrenees and the Sierra Morena were cut, as the mining operations required great quantities of wood for beams and for reducing metals from ores. Even ancient writers, such as Strabo in the first century B.C., speak of the widespread destruction by forest fires and suggest that the Pyrenees derived their name from the word fire — *pyr* — so long ago had this land been severely injured.

It is probably true that Spain made its first great advance as a *civilized* country through becoming a Roman province. However, the price of progress was severe because the Romans were mainly intent upon the extraction of the land's resources. Scars were left which time has not healed. Roman dominance came to an end with the fall of the Imperial City.

And now in the fifth century another human force was to beat upon this land — that of the Visigoths. In due course they conquered all of Spain except the southern strip, and took over where the Romans left off, in an attempt to reproduce a system of control as strict as that of Roman imperialism. This was a dour period lasting the better part of three centuries, and was finally terminated by the entrance of the Moors, the Berbers and the Arabs in the early years of the eighth century. There is little doubt that the Moslem ascendancy, which lasted for the better part of five centuries, was a period of rehabilitation both of land and of people. The latifundia system was abolished. The Moslems had a saying: "He who plants or sows, and who causes the earth to produce food for man or beast, does a service the account of which will be kept for him in heaven."

This attitude, accompanied by favorable changes in land tenure, did much to improve the country's agriculture. It was, too, a period of notable advancement in the arts and sciences and in the cultural progress of the people as a whole.

Eventually, however, there were two developments, occurring contemporaneously within the fifteenth and sixteenth centuries, which struck mortal blows to both people and land. The first was the conflict over religious and racial issues, reaching its climax in the Inquisition. The second was the passing of political power into the hands of the Mesta, the national association of sheep owners. This group came into a position of dominance with the encouragement of Ferdinand and Isabella. These rulers saw in the wool industry a great source of wealth for the Crown and for their country. For more than a century the sheep owners virtually monopolized the agricultural scene for their own purposes. The land was overgrazed, forests were burned off to provide extra pasturage, and the cycle of overuse and erosion was set into full motion. The power of the Mesta as a political organization lasted long enough to bring about severe damage to the agricultural regions of the country.

The fifteenth and sixteenth centuries were years of violent but transient glory. Spain's mariners, it is true, had gone to the far ends of the earth searching for those precious riches which their homeland had once contained. Her soldiers held strange people under subjugation with the tentacles of an octopus whose core-body, however, was in the last throes of its death spasm.

The end of the sixteenth century marked the eclipse of Spain as a dominant cultural and political force in the Western world. This culmination in the affairs of a vital people took place at the identical time that the land and resources of this once rich peninsula were finally reduced to the point of virtual exhaustion.

Spain reveals a story in which the harmonies and discords between man and man were transmitted, each in turn, to the very earth itself.

II. GREAT BRITAIN AND EUROPE

The twilight of empire ...
Where shall our people go?

How UNBELIEVABLE the course of events we are witnessing! "Rule, Britannia! Britannia, rule the waves!" Ah, no! This challenge of yesterday's world-dominant empire had a meaning far more profound than that of naval supremacy. It voiced the determination that the home country should be assured a continuing flow of resources — grain, beef and cotton from the Americas; mutton and wool from Australia and New Zealand; tea, rubber and spices from the Far East; and even diamonds and gold from South Africa. With a strong sense of predetermination, the British people developed their colonial empire for two reasons — the desirable one of establishing themselves as a great trading and banking center for the accumulation of capital and wealth, and, concurrently, the imperative one of maintaining lifelines through which there could be assured to her people the raw materials, including an ample food supply, with which to meet the needs of their expanding economy and rapidly growing population. Operation Britannia grew and succeeded during more than two centuries. Today it is weakened and imperiled because of profound, world-wide physical and social changes. Throughout its growing period during the eighteenth and nineteenth centuries, the trade of England rested largely upon the importing of raw materials in exchange for coal or the finished products from her factories that used coal for energy. Early in the present century, when petroleum came into general use, the coal of England and Wales began to lose its high premium value. The strength of England's economic structure simultaneously began to diminish.

One cannot generalize regarding the situation of European nations as a whole. Conditions from nation to nation vary considerably. A few are virtually self-supporting as far as food and other basic requirements for life are concerned. Consequently, such countries, assuming their populations are stabilized, can travel the path into the long future with good assurance that their peoples can maintain themselves. For instance, Denmark, Norway and Sweden are in relatively favorable positions. Belgium, fortified by its relationships with the Belgian Congo, is peculiarly fortunate just now. Although Belgium has one of the densest populations of Europe, her trade position and her per capita income promise her people a relatively satisfactory living standard under existing conditions. By a paradox, France, where the bogey of race suicide and underpopulation has existed for many years, is today considerably better off as to essential resources than many of its neighbors and is able to produce the bulk of the food required by its forty-two million inhabitants. In West Germany and Austria the situation has recently been made more difficult by the influx of more than nine million Germans from behind the iron curtain. There is a hopeful aspect in that her birth rate is one of the lowest in Europe, being about half the Continental average.

The situation of Holland is similar in many respects to that of Great Britain. It, too, is facing extremely difficult circumstances due in large part to a constantly increasing population combined with the loss of its possessions in the East Indies. Even since 1940 the per capita income of the Netherlands has dropped from the third highest in Europe to the eighth. We in the United States can better visualize Holland's situation in that, with ten million people, it has five times the population of South Carolina in half the area of that state. There is little possibility at the present time that the extremely dense and growing population of that country can avoid a drastic downward readjustment in its standard of living.

The contrasts in the ways of life of peoples living in close proximity could not be more vividly exemplified than by comparing the situation of Holland with that of Sweden. In the latter country, where religious dogma is virtually nonexistent, an experiment in population control is being made which has no parallel elsewhere.

Sweden bases its program on three principles. The first is that democracy implies voluntary parenthood and the right of the citizen to decide what his family should be; the second is that quantity of population should not be bought at the expense of quality; and the third is that the social and economic resources of society should be utilized to assure the maximum welfare of the maximum number of people. The initial legislation, which launched Sweden in its effort to deal with both the quantity and the quality of its population, was enacted in 1934 and was revised seven years later into the legislation that is now operative. One of the major purposes of this unique program is to prevent the bearing of children by parents who are mentally incompetent or physically defective. Sweden is daring to pioneer in one of the most essential problems of human society.

Whether we think it a small world or no, we need only to go to Italy, a mere thousand air-miles distant from Sweden, to find a dramatically opposite situation. Even the combination of beneficent climate and highly gifted people has not averted one bitter crisis after another in the long course of her history. One may say this is the way of all human life and the fate of all nations. Such is the pessimist's creed and the denial of the aspirations towards the realization of which humanity today, as never before, is justified in striving. As never before, however, causes will need to be dealt with rather than effects.

In her centuries of striving for peace and stability, Italy never discovered the "eternal equation" — that of a favorable balance between populations and resources. In the final days of the Roman Empire the dissolution was associated with the diminishment of available natural resources and, more specifically, with serious errors in land use. Today, the emphasis can be placed on the other factor in the equation — uncontrolled population growth and the almost intolerable pressures that accompany it.

Spain is met with a problem very similar to that of Italy — a vital people, more than twenty-seven million of them, increasing by two hundred thousand each year, hemmed in on their gaunt peninsula, greatly changed, as we have seen, from the days of its luminous ascendancy and world power. Had El Greco lived earlier, he would have painted in less austere forms and colors — his eyes saw an injured land, once as fertile and productive as any in Europe.

Slowly it is being recognized that plans must be developed through which resources can be more commonly shared. A generation ago no one would have dared to prophesy that the day could come when

France and Germany would pool their resources of coal and iron and enter into a compact of mutual use, or, in turn, that serious consideration would ever be given by the sixteen nations of Western Europe to establishing an agricultural and economic partnership. While it is true that much of the impulse for such action stems from the need to strengthen the position of Western Europe against the threat of Soviet force, nevertheless the fact remains that European nations are seeking to reduce the artificial barriers, imposed by national boundaries, to the exchange of natural resources.

Another example of the growth of the share-and-share-alike concept is that of the plan announced by the United States in 1949, spoken of as the "Point Four program," whose purpose is to extend certain advantages to other countries, especially those tabbed with the label "underdeveloped." From the American point of view the purpose of this program is, all in all, a sincere one, even though not solely altruistic, in that it stems from the realization that the better off other people are the better off we are. The golden rule in pragmatic form, one might say. This comment on the Point Four program has a somewhat cynical tone. It is not really so intended, because the *quid pro quo* principle is time-tested and sound enough, whether applied to morals, manners or materials! Regardless of its motives, the Point Four program holds within it the possibilities of marking a turning point towards a new epoch. It can meet with superb success if it washes itself clean of paternalism and of the careless assumption that the ways of the Western world, including the belief in industrialization as an ultimate panacea, are desirable for all people, everywhere.

The prevalent idea, especially in the United States, that industrialization in itself spells progress is fraught with danger and certainly is not one that can be universally adopted. The velocity of industrial expansion within the present century has had one consequence of extraordinary significance. It has resulted in a drain upon the earth's resources that has increased not upon an arithmetical scale related to population growth but upon a geometrical scale related to greater numbers of people demanding a greater variety of products from an increasingly complex industrial system. This fact, incidentally, bears directly upon the policies that are to guide the United States program for economic aid to underdeveloped countries. Unless, as is always questionable, adequate and long-continuing resource supply can be assured, industrialization is bound to end in ultimate failure. The most disillusioned man in the world is he who has had but a passing taste of a higher standard of living. Broadly speaking, the primary answer to the world's pressing needs will be found in the widespread improvement and development of agricultural practices, including the development of new sources of food supply. A factory is a disconsolate place for a starving body.

An example of the influence of a so-called physical change, here meaning the change in the use of a natural resource, is the disrupting effect that the discovery of petroleum has had on the economy of Great Britain. The need of the British to gain control of another fuel resource led them, among other courses, into developing extensive oil reserves in Iran and other foreign lands. The dispute between the British owners and the Iranian government has, in recent years, been a focal point of international tension. Stripped to its stark essentials, it represents a conflict over the ownership of a single resource, relatively limited in amount and within the boundaries of one of the smaller nations — a conflict that has contained the germs of being the explosive origin of war.

The episode of the British in Iran has many counterparts, involving not only the continuance of colonial empires by the nations of Western Europe but also the rights of large corporations, whether in Europe or the United States, to the use or development of resources in countries other than their own. Equity and justice as regards the ownership and use of resources are obviously fundamental to peace. One cannot escape the conclusion that we have entered an era when new conceptions must be adopted and that the changes which are even now taking place will have far-reaching social and political consequences. Growing recognition of this by the nations of the free world is one of the brightest signs in the present convulsive period of human history.

Now as to the population situation in Europe as a whole, we may gain perspective by recalling the amazing growth in the numbers of its peoples in recent times. Although it has its advantages, it is a pity, in a way, that the concept of *time* is so elusive to all of us. We think of a century ago as if it were an astronomical *X* in time space, bearing no relation to ourselves. Actually, it represents the birth time of parents of many of us living today. It is barely possible to visualize the rapidity of historical change unless, by some trick of the mind, we personalize it.

The reasons for population growth are several, but, in large part, are a result of the remarkable advances in sanitation and medical care that occurred concurrently with economic expansion and the development of transportation. Irrespective of causes, an analysis of which is a study in itself, the fact is that the present population of Europe, exclusive of Russia, numbering about four hundred million, is double that of a hundred years ago, almost triple that of the year 1800, and more than five times that of the middle of the seventeenth century.

It might be observed that six generations represent merely the span of two full lifetimes — Western style. Only that long ago the British, the French and the

Dutch were establishing their colonial empires in Asia, the Near East and Africa. Today the former two stand precariously at Suez, in Tunisia and in Viet-Nam, while the Dutch have "settled" back in their own country. Within the drive for freedom and independence, and within the surges of ideological change, is the detonating power of another reality, the demand of hard-pressed, expanding populations that their resources, including their food resources, be retained for themselves.

The irony of events, when the nation classically spoken of as the "beef eaters" is now reduced to an individual ration of tenpence worth of meat per week! The rich surpluses, including those of food supply, that England could once draw from her colonies and other far countries, no longer exist. The insurance of a dependable supply of resources that the establishment of the British Commonwealth was intended to provide has been dissolved by circumstances beyond the control of any political structure. The fivefold increase in the population of Great Britain within a century and a half has been paralleled and even exceeded in her own colonies as well as in many countries throughout the world. Their export gates are slowly closing to protect the needs of their own people. The roll can be called — Australia, New Zealand, India, Canada, South Africa, Argentina, Egypt, her neighbors in Europe! Few, if any, can or will respond. It is a long cry indeed from the time of which the historian Trevelyan could write: "The fact that our island grew most of its own food and also commanded the paths of the ocean was the dual basis 'of Britain's calm felicity and power' which Wordsworth viewed with a just complacency as he gazed upon sea and land together from the summit of Black Comb."

The quandary of Great Britain and of some of the countries in Europe whose lifelines to colonies are threatened or already severed can be resolved only by readjustments of extraordinary difficulty. The practice of denial and austerity is a beautiful thing in principle, but grim for peoples who have become accustomed to a high level of economic welfare.

Within the last two or three years a great deal has been said or written regarding emigration as a solution to the problem of overpopulation in Great Britain and Europe. The arguments for such a program are persuasive and, when presented in a diagram or blueprint, appear captivatingly simple. One needs to remember, however, the oft-proven difficulty of removing people from their homelands. As a general rule people prefer to *die* at home rather than *live* somewhere else, no matter how enticing the prospects are made to appear. The historical efforts of European governments to organize emigration on a large scale have been uniformly unsuccessful. Even Mussolini was unable to establish more than fifteen thousand Italians in the colony he created in northern Africa; and efforts towards a large-scale re-settlement of Italians in Ethiopia, had this land continued as an Italian colony, would probably have proved equally unsuccessful.

An earlier example is Germany, before the First World War, whose colonial empire had less than twenty-five thousand German inhabitants. The migrations of peoples, whether to move to better lands or to escape persecution at home, have invariably sprung from spontaneous and voluntary actions. Any substantial program of emigration from the countries of Europe could presumably only be accomplished through governmental compulsion. It may come to that, but it is as well to recognize the fact in advance. And then there is the other side of the matter. To what lands could Europeans be moved? Some of the observations elsewhere in this book may throw light on that question.

The idea of large-scale planned emigration of people from Europe needs, however, to be approached even more directly. Would the proposals that are currently being made relieve the pressures of populations that Great Britain and Europe are now experiencing?

The first condition to be recognized is that Europe's population is presently increasing at the rate of approximately three million a year. While Europe, without considering European Russia, is, as a whole, slowly trending towards a stabilized population, it is evident that many millions more will still be added to this already overcrowded continent.

A new science was born not so long ago. It is called "demography," and while, strictly, it is supposed to be that branch of sociology that treats of the statistics of births and deaths, it is evolving, as it should, into the study of the relationship of peoples with their environments, including, of course, their resources. If the human race is fortunate, this science, under whatever name, should grow and become widely recognized as one of the most potent and useful that has ever served mankind. But today it is still young, and even some of its basic terms are not yet clearly definable. One of these terms is "optimum population," implying the most desirable number of people who can live in any given region to the maximum satisfaction and welfare of all.

In light of the above what is an optimum population for Europe? If the term is not explicit, certainly no answer can yet be given that would receive general acceptance. However, the specter of overpopulation has haunted Europe for a century or more. Far worse, it has been the excuse, if not the cause, of her two last consuming wars, whether resting upon the *Lebensraum* (living-room) theory of the Germans or the "have nots vs. haves" theory of Mussolini. Any "optimum" figure, therefore, would need to be arbitrarily selected and would continue to be theoretical if it were not based upon a series of carefully studied quotas of constituent regions and countries. Unquestionably mankind is being forced to the need of making such computations.

One could argue, for instance, that it would be well if Europe's population could be set back to the level of 1925. Since that year the Continent's agricultural productivity has not greatly changed, her trading position has, if anything, lost ground and the era of colonialism is coming to an end. Yet Europe now has almost fifty million more people than she had twenty-five years ago, and this despite the casualties and removals of peoples that resulted from World War II. All one might infer is that Europe has already passed beyond her optimum and, with continuing increases in her numbers, is departing further from this elusive yet infinitely desirable condition. No wonder there is the insistent cry for emigration as the answer to her enigma.

The evidence indicates that emigration should not be relied upon as the answer. For one thing, sixty million people have migrated from Europe since the beginning of the nineteenth century; yet this substantial movement of peoples, frequently exceeding more than a million in a single year, has not proved a deterrent to the threefold increase of the aggregate population that has occurred within the same period. The best example refuting the idea that emigration may be the safety valve which can adequately relieve population pressure is that of Italy. It is estimated that more than fifteen million Italians have left their homeland within the last century. Yet during most of this time Italy's population growth at home has been among the highest in Europe. The case of Sicily is especially revealing. Her rate of emigration has been almost twice that of the Italian mainland. Nevertheless, her population has increased considerably faster than that of Italy proper.

It should be noted that the above figure, indicating the aggregate number of Italians that have emigrated from their own country within the century, cannot be accepted as being entirely accurate because many emigrants returned eventually to pass their declining years in the country of their birth — a rather touching commentary on the deep-rooted and pervasive affection of people for their homeland. Nevertheless, by far the greater part of those who emigrated remained in the countries of their adoption.

In the United States, for example, the 1940 census recorded more than 1,600,000 people born in Italy even though the rate of immigration was drastically reduced after the introduction of the quota system in 1924. Between 1900 and 1914, the peak of Italian immigration, there was not a single year during which less than a hundred thousand Italians entered the United States. The overall number of Italians who came to this country from 1820 to 1950 is 4,776,884, though some of these returned to their homeland. In Argentina, one third of the country's population is of Italian origin; South

Brazil has also received a large number of Italian immigrants during the last seventy-five years.

Irrespective of facts such as the above, let us assume that a program of emigration would somewhat relieve, if not cure, the pressures of population which most European countries, as well as Great Britain, are now experiencing. The question at once arises — to what countries could Europeans desirably emigrate? Under present conditions, Asia, Soviet Russia and the countries under its control, as well as the countries in the Near East, are out of the question. Quite apart from ideologies, Asia and the Near East have a far more critical population problem than Europe. Consequently possible open spaces exist only in North or South America, in Africa or in Australia. Considerable attention will be given in the following chapters to analyzing the potentialities of these regions.

III. AUSTRALIA, CANADA AND ARGENTINA

Food-surplus countries —
delusions and realities

O PEN SPACES in which migrating people could establish new homes are of little value unless they promise adequate food supply. A recent annual report of the United Nations Food and Agriculture Organization states that only five countries are capable of producing more food today than their own people need: Australia, New Zealand, Canada, Argentina and the United States. This same report brings out a fact of extraordinary importance. It is that the increase in the world food supply is not keeping pace with population growth, or, expressed explicitly, that total world food production is now merely 9 per cent greater than the average in the years 1934–1938, while the number of the world's people is 12 per cent greater. This fateful gap is widening in many countries despite an almost universal effort to close it.

In the last few years most of the designs for effecting mass movements of people from Europe have been made by an organization known as the International Refugee Organization, an affiliate of the United Nations. It originally came into existence for the laudable and urgent purpose of taking care of the hundreds of thousands, indeed millions, of suffering people who had been made homeless during the violence of the Second World War. Its services in that emergency were invaluable. Latterly, a successor organization, the Intergovernmental Committee for European Migration, is giving attention to this problem of relieving Europe's population pressures — a quite different objective from that with which the IRO originally dealt. Its recent report proposes to "solve the crisis" by shifting five million Europeans during the next decade to "labor-short" countries. By a strange coincidence the countries designated in this report as "labor-short" are identical with those described by the United Nations Food and Agriculture Organization as being "food-long" (with one exception: the report cites Latin America, and not solely Argentina). Obviously a food-long country is not necessarily labor-short, or vice versa. A primary requirement of any emigration program is to make sure that people go to countries that produce more food than their own people need. It would be much better to make this clear. How incorrect, too, to use the phrase "solve the crisis." This world problem is too acute to permit a careless use of words that can too easily create false optimism. At the current rate of increase, Europe's population will total more than 430,000,000 in ten years, despite promising evidences of declining birth rates in at least a few countries. The proposed emigration program would prove an antidote but not a cure.

In the following series of observations regarding the so-called "food-long" countries — commencing with Australia — it will be noted that one or more of them already have population densities that are even now pressing upon their capacities of food production. However, there are extensive areas such as the Amazon Basin or parts of Africa that might qualify as the open spaces that are so greatly needed. Consequently consideration will be given to these other potential regions in later chapters.

Is Australia today actually in a position to produce more food than her own people need? In responding to this question it would be desirable to look at this country in some detail because it happens to exemplify vividly two conditions: first, the unfavorable effects of overindustrialization, second, the stern barrier that blocks the productive capacity of any country whose water resources are limited.

The first condition has changed Australia from being an important food-exporting country to one that now is really troubled as to whether she can feed her own population. At the same time her aspiration to become a great exporter of manufactured products has not materialized, so that now her principal commodities for export are reduced to wool and minerals and the country is running a substantial trading deficit.

This state of affairs stems from the misconception that in the modern world industrialization is the one and ultimate goal. This point of view first began to influence the actions of the government and people of Australia several decades ago, but has really dominated their policies during the last decade. As one economist, Colin Clark, well versed in Australian affairs, expresses it:

> It was believed that in the post-war world there would be no food problem other than the disposal of unmarketable surpluses; that the quicker the farm population could be shifted into the city the better; that Australian manufacturers were going to have a wonderful time producing everything which had been previously imported; that we would, in fact, probably import very little except tea and petrol, and would be exporters of steel, textiles, and motorcars; that the Japanese economy would virtually disappear, and that Australian industry would dominate oriental markets. All this egregious rubbish was eagerly accepted by the Australian public, who found that it fitted exactly into their social and political preconceptions. "Demos like any other tyrant, can only be told what he wants to hear." These preconceptions were shared by all political parties and by all sections of the community.

Australia therefore pursued a policy of industrialisation which has given us more factory workers relative to our population than the United States has, but with the average product per man-hour about one-third of the American level and with our economy more dependent upon imports than ever before. . . .

Since the war Australia has done everything she could to give priority to manufacturers, at the expense of farm and pastoral production. Not only has labor been drawn from the country into the cities; the rural producer has been kept short of galvanised iron and wire (necessary materials under Australian conditions) in order to give priority to urban requirements. When the 40-hour week was introduced in 1947 one prominent Government representative urged in its favour that it would assist in the desirable process of closing down farms and bringing more people into the cities.

Price control regulations, by both Federal and State Governments, have been used to keep the prices of foodstuffs as low as possible, while allowing the prices of manufactures to rise comparatively freely.

One is presumably justified in believing that inasmuch as these troubles are of Australia's own making they can be cleared up if the government and people make up their minds to do so. All the while the population of the country is growing, largely by immigration, at the substantial rate of 3 per cent per annum (Australia's present population is approximately eight and a half millions). There are, of course, considerable differences of opinion as to the size of the population that Australia may eventually be able to provide for, assuming satisfactory conditions of food supply, housing and employment. With a change in present policies, including the vitally needed development of agriculture, some believe that a population of forty millions by the century's end is a reasonable figure to anticipate.

The principal lesson to be learned from the present Australian situation is, obviously, the serious penalties that result from overemphasis upon industrialization. The needed reorientation of this country's point of view, involving a change-about in attitude of government and people, will take a lot of doing. Even if this effort on the human side meets with success, there are reasons for questioning whether Australia will be capable of increasing her food production, now scarcely adequate for her present population of eight and a half millions, to a volume that will meet the needs of the hypothetical forty millions by the century's end.

The second condition mentioned above, that of water resources, will have a distinct bearing upon the question of how large a population Australia can sustain. This great subcontinent, lying in the far reaches of the southwest Pacific, is a deceptive place. After all, its size is almost exactly that of the United States, and at first glance it seems peculiar, to say the least, that so extensive a land area is actually beginning to find difficulty in producing enough food for a population scarcely larger than that of New York City! Australia is an arch example of a country whose capacity for agriculture production is inexorably limited by scarcity of natural water supply.

A recent official report provides this illuminating classification of Australia's total land surface of approximately 1,904,000,000 acres:

34 per cent with an erratic annual rainfall of less than ten inches. This area is mainly desert, but a part of it is capable of carrying an extremely sparse livestock population.

42 per cent has sufficient rainfall to provide fair to good grazing, but insufficient for producing crops.

16½ per cent, although within zones where rainfall is satisfactory for cropping, is either in the form of mountains or barren highlands, or has unsuitable soils.

7½ per cent (about 144 million acres) has climate, soils and topography suitable for cropping and intensive livestock production. Allowing for permanent pastures and for fallow and temporary pastures, this could perhaps mean an upper limit of between 36 and 48 million acres to the total area which could be put under crop annually. The area under crop in 1949–1950 was 20½ million acres.

This report points out that advances in farming techniques may, in the future, result in a more favorable classification of land capacity. The introduction of new leguminous pastures or further discoveries in soil chemistry could, for example, make it possible to develop, for intensive use, soils at present regarded as unsuitable. A recent observer from the United States believes that improved results could be gained if a more critical consideration were given to when and how rain falls, in other words if planting were better timed to periods of precipitation. Further, there is little doubt that adaptation of the dry-farming methods used in the western plains regions of both Canada and the United States would add considerably to Australia's agricultural output.

Even after allowing for all such possible improvements, however, the above classification of Australia's land resources makes clear the limitations imposed by the climatic environment of the country upon the expansion of its agricultural production. This is all the more striking when it is considered that in the arid and semiarid areas, comprising about three quarters of the continent's total land area, the problem is not so much one of expanding as of maintaining levels of production. The loss of natural vegetation in these areas from overstocking and the selective feeding habits of rabbits — a scourge in Australia — has resulted in a permanent reduction of their carrying capacity. In the Western Division of New South Wales, for example, the sheep population is now less than half the numbers carried fifty years ago, and cattle herds have also had to be considerably reduced.

As is to be expected, there is considerable current stir aimed at the extension of irrigation as a means of developing the rural resources of Australia. Schemes are afoot to tap the Burdekin River in Queensland, the Glenelg and Loddon Rivers in Victoria; and a major project, the Snowy Mountains Authority, for both water and power development, is under way in New South Wales. While such plans are, so to speak, "mandatory," the ultimate effect needs to be judged from a relative point of view. As has recently been pointed out by the Rural Reconstruction Commission, the potential irrigable land in Australia is far more limited than is popularly supposed. These limitations arise not only from the water supply available but also from the problems of storage capacity and distribution. It is estimated that, with a full development of the country's resources, the present acreage under irrigation could be tripled and brought up eventually to five million acres. This sounds impressive until one realizes that the United States irrigates over twenty-five million acres where rainfall is deficient, out of a total cropland area of four hundred million acres. No, the climatic limitations upon Australia are severe.

All in all, there is justified and growing uneasiness there. Land planted to wheat has decreased by more than two million acres in the last five years, beef exports are a third less than prewar and butter exports almost a half less. Recent articles in the Melbourne press carry such headlines as, HUNGER AHEAD? — RE-MEMBER THE LAND — DANGER OF FAMINE. If this is scare journalism it is journalism with a purpose, based not upon fantasy but upon facts that have to be coped with, as in time they can and presumably will be. Yet, even under the most favorable of future developments, two facts stand clear: there are obvious limits to the home population that Australia can support; and, secondly, those countries, either in the British Commonwealth or outside it, that in recent decades have relied upon receiving substantial and sustained Australian exports of foodstuffs have, to express it mildly, ample reason for concern.

New Zealand is undoubtedly a country of some potential but it should not be looked upon as a contributor of any major importance to the world's food needs. After all, it is relatively small, its total land area being equal only to that of the state of Colorado in the United States or to one half of that of France. Its inclusion as one of the world's five food-long countries is accurate enough but, at the same time, of minor significance as far as the world situation is concerned.

Canada, by contrast, is a country of large potential, especially for minerals, forest products and marine resources. Its expansion of economic activity is proceeding with great speed, and in the twelve years following the beginning of World War II its rate of economic development exceeded even that of the United States.

In this short time the manufacture of pulp and paper nearly doubled, the production of aluminum increased five times, the recovery of petroleum six times and that of iron ore thirty-eight times. What the eventual consequences of this rapidly accelerating consumption of resources may be is not directly within our consideration here. The implications, however, are not unlike those that will be touched upon in the next chapter, which reveal that the United States is awakening to find itself facing critical shortages in a number of key materials.

Canada, during the twelve years since the beginning of World War II, has had a population increase of 21 per cent, from 11,600,000 to 14,000,000 and has increased its agricultural production by 22 per cent. There are apt to be delusions, however, concerning the agricultural possibilities of Canada. Only about 10 per cent of its land is suitable for agriculture. At the present time, the country has 90,000,000 acres of land under cultivation and in addition some 50,000,000 acres of natural pasturage and range land. It is estimated that with the development of the remaining northern areas, where climate and economic production are limiting factors, the maximum potential of arable land in Canada on which a self-sustaining agriculture could be maintained would aggregate 130,000,000 acres. For purposes of comparison this adds up to less than one third of the agricultural lands of the United States.

While Canada's Prairie Provinces are well suited to the extensive cultivation of wheat and other grains, it would be a grave error to compare, either as to sheer size or as to quality, Canada's breadbasket with that of the United States. Because of the geologic configuration of the North American continent, the great region in the United States of the interior lowlands, extending approximately from the western slopes of the Appalachians to the eastern edge of the Great Plains, does not exist in Canada. A vast rock mass of great age, known as the Laurentian Shield, blankets all of Quebec north of the Saint Lawrence Valley, all of Ontario north of the Ontario Peninsula, as well as the territory north of the Lakes Huron and Superior and a sizable portion of Manitoba east of Lake Winnipeg. Consequently, as one travels westward, it is found that Canada's really productive agricultural lands do not begin until one reaches beyond the 96° meridian, or the longitude of North Dakota, Nebraska, or central Kansas. In brief, Canada does not possess the equivalent of the great corn belt in the United States, which, through its corn-hog and corn-cattle economy, provides so large a part of the American diet.

Almost all of agricultural Canada is handicapped by being subject to severe late frosts in spring and early frosts in fall, which, at intervals, cause widespread damage to crops. Frost has occurred in every month of the year *nearly everywhere*. This frost boundary sharply limits the length of the growing season in Canada. The average frost-free period in the Prairie Provinces is 90 days; this is but an average, for it is 60 days along the northern margins of agriculture and up to 110 days in the south. Further, the southernmost, and especially the southwesternmost, parts of the grain belt in Canada do not have the rich black soil (chernozem) which runs in a northwestward direction from Winnipeg toward Saskatoon and Edmonton, Alberta. There are actually some very poor lands with some badland topography along the Saskatchewan–Montana border.

The annual precipitation in the prairies of Canada averages less than fifteen inches a year and through most of the grain belt less than twenty inches. The output from the wheat belt in Canada, as in the United States, is subject to annual fluctuations depending upon the adequacy of the rainfall along the ever-shifting drought boundary of the 100° meridian. Therefore, it is no surprise to find that there are substantial differences year by year in the total grain crops of both countries, with the United States in the more favorable position because the threat of unseasonable frosts is far less. The United States has a further natural advantage because, in addition to its spring-wheat belt, which lies immediately south of Canada's, it has a highly productive winter-wheat belt to the south, centering on the state of Kansas. In this region climatic conditions are quite different from those to the north. Consequently, poor yields in the spring-wheat belt do not necessarily imply a poor year in the winter-wheat belt, and thus the United States is frequently capable of balancing out its annual output, whereas Canada cannot. While Canada is one of the world's more important agricultural producers today and holds distinct possibilities for further development, it would be an error to over-magnify its potentialities. Climate is a stern master despite the will of man.

In passing, the comment is quite often made that the American farmer is not doing so competent a job as some farmers in Europe, where, in several countries, the number of bushels of grain produced per acre is frequently very much larger than that in the United States or Canada. It is, therefore, assumed that the rate of crop production in the United States as well as in Canada can and should be considerably higher. This assumption is not fully justified. The farmer in the better agricultural regions in Europe has the advantage of a more temperate climate, a more dependable rain supply and less threat of frosts.

As to Argentina, traditionally one of the world's greatest exporters of foodstuffs, events in recent years have brought her to a condition very similar to that of Australia. Her whole agricultural position has changed drastically for the worse. The fact that this has happened in both countries is the more startling when one bears in mind how different they are racially and culturally, and, above all, how unlike in their political organization — the one a government by dictatorship, the other by democratic (or popular) representation. The truth is that both countries exemplify the strong trend in modern times to overemphasize industrialization at the expense of agriculture. Obviously they are not alone in doing this — other countries are risking the same dangers. It just so happens that both Australia and Argentina are the clearest present examples of the critical consequences of such a policy. They provide a warning, by the way, in regard to programs that may be applied to so-called "underdeveloped" countries. The protection and encouragement of the agricultural base is a *sine qua non* — this ancient phrase in this case can be accepted almost literally: "Without which — nothing!"

Argentina, by its natural endowments, is one of the most fertile regions on the earth. The Argentine pampas, until lately, have produced large surpluses of wheat, corn, flaxseed, and fodder, and have raised more cattle than even the meat-loving Argentines could consume. Because of the pampas' proximity to the major seaports of Buenos Aires, Rosario, and La Plata, the Argentines have held competitive advantage in world markets over practically all other exporters of agricultural surpluses.

It is one of the major disappointments of this postwar era that wealthy Argentina is no longer able to help to fill the ever-widening gap between food and people in many of the less fortunate parts of the world. By 1949 the acreage planted to the principal export crops stood at but 65 per cent of the area planted to these crops ten years earlier. The severe two-year drought during 1950–1951 has, unfortunately, carried this decline even further.

What are the causes of Argentina's plight? What is it that forced a nation accustomed to a diet of two hundred pounds of meat per capita per year suddenly to institute a regime of meatless days in 1952? The accusing finger points first and foremost to the policies of the present government. In order to carry out the program of industrialization and self-sufficiency, it has left agriculture by the wayside. The gist of the story is that the government has been running the country at the expense of the farmer. With the aid of a government purchasing and exporting monopoly, agricultural products are bought at cutthroat prices and disposed of to the highest overseas bidder. The profits thus realized go into the dictator-government's coffers and are used, in large part, to further popular and vote-getting social welfare measures. Whatever the official excuse for such a program, it has resulted in general apathy on the land. Lacking the incentive to produce and denied the foreign exchange necessary to acquire badly needed agricultural machinery from abroad, farmers are turning out poor crops and have been migrating in ever-growing numbers toward the cities where, under the slogan of rapid industrialization, factory workers are being pampered by artificially high wages.

Inflation has been the inevitable result of repeated wage boosts without an accompanying increase in labor productivity. Between 1950 and 1952 the cost of living rose by 12 per cent in the United States; in Argentina it rose by 73 per cent to top an inflationary spiral which appears greater than that in any other country during the same period. Because these developments have been especially unfavorable to the farmer, there is today a shortage of farm labor, and this decline in man power has not been offset by increased mechanization or by improved farming techniques. While immigration from Europe since the end of World War II has averaged over a hundred thousand persons annually, little has been done until the last year or two to direct newcomers to agricultural work. The Perón government is now trying to cure a situation for which only itself can be blamed. It is hard to say whether it can be successful in doing this. The tide has run far in the wrong direction.

The lack of financial incentive has also contributed heavily to the decay of rural economy, and in some sections of the famous black-soil pampas, farmlands are taking on the aspect of the American dust bowl of the 1930's. The depths to which agriculture has fallen are evidenced by the fact that there is now a shortage of cattle feed, and that, therefore, scraggly six-month-old bullocks must be slaughtered in Argentina's famed *frigoríficos*. The Argentine meat-packing industry fell 25 per cent short of its promised deliveries of two hundred thousand tons of meat scheduled for Britain during the trade year ended April 1952.

Even before the beginning of heavy rural-urban migration induced by Perón policies, Argentina was a strongly urbanized nation — too much so for one whose principal wealth lies in agriculture. According to the 1947 census, only 38.6 per cent of the country's population lived on farms or in towns under two thousand. Consequently, Argentina today shows as large an urban majority as does the United States, the world's most industrialized nation. Inevitably, therefore, more and more of the country's arable acres will be planted in crops for urban domestic consumption and in crops that are suitable for industrial use.

All the while the situation in Argentina, as in so many countries, is being aggravated by the rapid and continuing growth of its population. Today the country has eighteen million people, or more than double what it had only thirty-eight years ago. Far more formidable is the fact that the current rate of increase is so high that the country is now adding more than four hundred thousand to its population each year. These growing pressures might be comfortably absorbed if the country's agricultural and industrial economy were in sounder balance. As it is, a population increase of such magnitude tends to accenutate the difficulties which this country faces.

Dictators may come and go and there will be alternating periods of droughts and of bumper crops. Yet the present urge for self-sufficiency and economic independence, bred by nationalism, will presumably continue for years to come. Throughout the world, the so-called "underdeveloped" nations are breaking away from the one-crop economy, which in the past has exposed them to the mercy of world market fluctuations. Right or wrong, Argentina is a notable example of a nation ridding itself of a "colonial" economy, and, by moving too rapidly in the opposite direction, threatening its own food supply and at the same time depriving the world of badly needed food surpluses.

IV. THE UNITED STATES

*What of the land of
"endless resources"?*

To what degree may we Americans be compelled increasingly to concern ourselves with the question of the numbers of our people and their needs? Could it be that the influence of the "eternal equation" is already beginning to be felt in this great country of seemingly endless resources?

A response to these questions may be given by referring first to our population, then to our agriculture and, finally, to certain factors that have a bearing on our industrial economy as well as on our general standard of living. There is news on all three fronts — some of it, until very recently, quite unforeseen.

The fact is that we are now facing an entirely unexpected outlook in regard to our own population — one that will inevitably prove of far-reaching social and economic significance. The idea that our population was about to reach a peak and would then either level off, or even decline, became general in the 1930's. In that decade both birth rates and death rates appeared to have stabilized and immigration had virtually ceased. One of the widely accepted projections, issued in 1938, placed our peak population at 140,000,000, to be reached in the year 1960; another placed the peak, to be reached about 1980, at 154,000,000. Already we have gone considerably above the latter figure. As recently as 1947 one authority viewed with optimism the anticipated decline in our population and expressed the opinion that our economic optimum population was well below the current level and perhaps even as low as 100,000,000. Even as late as 1949, it was generally expected that our peak population would be 165,000,000, with strong indications of a decline from this figure before the end of the century. Every one of these forecasts now has to be discarded — all have been proved erroneous.

This wholly unexpected change in our population expectancy has resulted from three unforeseen circumstances: somewhat larger immigration, a continuing decline in the death rate, and, lastly, the predominating factor of a sharp and sustained upsurge in the birth rate. It would be out of place here to present analyses or details of these three factors that are of such profound significance to the future of our country. The gist of the situation today is that our present rate of increase is averaging two and a half million people each year.

As to longer range prospects, a recent estimate, made by an economist who was obviously unperturbed by the errors of earlier forecasts, envisages that our population at the end of the century will stand within a range of a low figure of 200,000,000 and a high of 300,000,000. This seems an extreme view, and, in any case, such projections need not have first call on our considerations here. It is sufficient to take the now generally accepted opinion that our population will reach a figure of at least 190,000,000 by the year 1975 — or 30,000,000 more people than we have today.

This prospect poses a host of questions, such as the physical functioning of ever-larger cities, the increased costs of various forms of social welfare, and the added load upon an educational system which, in many respects, is incapable of meeting present demands. In one way or another such problems will be solved, though how satisfactorily remains to be seen. The essential question, the one first to consider, will still remain: can our farmlands produce sufficient food for this substantial increase in our numbers? In seeking the answer, we might start with the comforting assurance that it is highly unlikely that our newspapers will be running HUNGER AHEAD headlines similar to those frequently appearing in Australian newspapers. The food-producing capacity of our country is so great that it is illogical to anticipate a food crisis, at least within the period of which we are now thinking. Further, the diet standard of the American people as a whole is relatively so high that moderate downward adjustments could be made without physical ill effect. However, it should be mentioned that the diet of a fairly considerable number of people in this country is not up to a desirable standard. Diet, like any other day-by-day matter, becomes habitual, and it is within the measure of existing levels that any appraisals as to food or other living standards need to be considered. In this light it is certainly not assured that the food requirements of this country's population twenty odd years from now will be met — to say nothing of our having surplus food for export.

At the present time croplands, plus land devoted to livestock used for food supplies, aggregates 464,000,000 acres. The latest computations prepared by the United States Department of Agriculture, submitted in testimony before Congress in 1952, indicate that the amount of land that will be needed to provide food at present diet levels for our anticipated population in the year 1975, including provision for our present export surplus, adds up to the formidable figure of 577,000,000 acres. This represents 113,000,000 more acres than are now in use and, in turn, 70,000,000 acres more than are envisioned in all presently projected governmental programs for land development and reclamation. It is not easy to face facts such as these in the country of "endless resources." We have about come to land's end.

Several counteracting trends will affect the outcome. For example, continuing improvements in technology on the farms can be counted upon. How substantial they may be in the future nobody can tell. Without minimizing their great importance in recent years and especially their promise for the years ahead, such improved techniques cannot alone work the miracle. Judged by the record, official estimates indicate that the application of such techniques have, during the last thirteen years, resulted in a gain the equivalent of production from 64,000,000 acres of land. A steady, year-by-year improvement, at the same average pace as that of the last decade, will have to occur if we are to meet future needs. It is our last remaining substitute for the surplus land we no longer have.

On the other hand, strong negative forces will also be at work. Principal among these is the fact that we have by no means won the fight against soil erosion. In the country as a whole the quality of our soils continues to deteriorate. Recent government studies in the large area of highly productive soils in the Midwest result in an estimate that the inherent productivity of soils in this great region is going downhill at the rate of $\frac{7}{10}$ of 1 per cent a year, and a study made in Iowa indicates a deterioration in that state of 1 per cent a year. Such estimates represent trends, nothing more, a slow process of corrosion that eventually, in the long future, will prove an increasingly weakening factor upon our people and our country. Such trends can somehow be checked, but up to this time, with all the progress of recent years, enough has not yet been accomplished.

The day is still to come when we realize that the protection of our agricultural base is the first need of a "national defense" program. By this is meant not military defense but the defense of values that make American life what it is.

This great change in the outlook of this country's food supply will finally do away with the fantasy that "America can feed the world." Of course no one quite believed this; yet there has been a vague popular impression that, if the need came, we could relieve a food crisis in another country out of our own great abundance. For instance, in the last few years the threat of widespread famine in India has naturally been a matter of grave concern and it has been frequently assumed that, if the worst came to the worst, America could stand by to pull that country through any sudden emergency. Illustrating the virtual impossibility of such action under any circumstances, India, during 1951, endeavored to import six million tons of grain in order to take care of her shortage. This would be enough to feed about thirty million people, or about 8 per cent of her total population. Naturally, her efforts were directed towards obtaining as much as she could from countries not too far distant, including China, in order to reduce the costs of transportation from faraway sources. In passing, it is well for the Western world to realize that, in face of such needs, the present Indian government has reasons more compelling than ideology in her attitude towards the Communist government of China. "Food comes first" is an agelong motive.

The idea that the United States could carry India through what will presumably be mounting food crises is so unrealistic that it is a pity it is ever talked of seriously. A revealing article recently published on the Indian situation throws a sidelight on this aspect of the matter. India's need of six million tons in the year 1951 is obviously a huge amount of grain. It would require six hundred large ships, of at least five hundred feet in length, to carry it, with the dispatch of two such ships per day during an entire year. No — much as another nation may wish to help, and indeed ardently may try, the eventual answers to India's crushing problem of imbalance between her resources and her people must be found, in the main, within her own country.

Returning to our own situation, there is an element in our natural-resource picture that is commencing to reach the critical point. This is water supply. With the surprise that comes from any new experience, some forty million Americans, living in various regions and communities, are now face to face with problems of water — either those of real shortage, or of unsatisfactory quality, or both. During the last fifty years our per capita consumption of water has doubled, and in view of the fact that our population has also doubled during this period it is evident that our water needs have increased four times since 1900. While a part of this use is due, of course, to domestic and municipal demands, the larger part is due to the tremendous drafts that are being placed on water by the growth of industry and the extension of agriculture, including huge irrigation projects. An isolated statistic, in itself, does not mean much, but it is of incidental interest that the present per capita use of water — in other words, the estimated total use throughout the nation for all purposes, divided by the number of our people — runs to the extraordinary quantity of 1200 gallons each day! Shades of yesteryear, when a couple of buckets a day per person in any homestead did very well. Sanitary facilities, washing machines and a score of other personal conveniences, including such luxuries as air conditioning, have changed all that. Time does not move backward — we can presumably be glad of that — and so it is that water, and lots of it, has now become part of the American way of life.

These brief references to water will at least serve to indicate how essential it is, and how powerful its influence will be upon industrial and population trends. The combination of a fairly high average rainfall and the superb natural arteries of large inland rivers and lakes in many regions of our country has deluded the majority of us into believing that water is one resource about which we in the United States need have no concern. Consequently a water problem is a brand new experience to many Americans. In terms of the maintenance of our existing standard of living, the question of adequacy of water supply is bound to be one of increasing importance. We can, indeed we will, be forced to adopt better practices in the development and use of this country's water resources; but, even then, water, and not only crops, forest products or mineral resources, will prove a limiting factor to population and industrial expansion.

The relationship between agriculture and a highly industrialized society such as that of the United States is frequently overlooked. At first thought, for instance, an automobile plant seems an operation quite remote from that of a farm. Statistics should generally be given with the same reluctance as they are apt to be read, but these which follow so strikingly illustrate the industry–farm relationship that the antistatistics impulse which most of us feel might be put aside for a moment. It has been computed that the manufacture of a million automobiles requires:

89,000,000 pounds of cotton, the crop from 558,000 acres, for making upholstery, brake-linings, timing gears and safety glass;

500,000 bushels of maize, the harvest of 11,280 acres, for rubber substitute, butyl alcohol and solvents;

damental assumption to the effect that the rate of growth of our economy in the next twenty-five years will be neither more nor less that what it has been in the past. A 3 per cent rate of growth, compounded, results in a doubling every 25 years. Consequently, it is assumed that the total output of goods and services in the United States, the gross national product, will, by the year 1975, be twice what it actually was in 1950.

With this assumption in mind, the report than goes on to project the general magnitude of demand in the decade 1970–1980 for various major raw materials. It recognizes that a doubling of the gross national product does not imply that actually twice the amount of materials will be required, because part of the values represented in measuring national production are based upon an increased amount of fabrication and a greater proportion of services. Even then it is envisaged that our present tremendous usage of natural resources will be increased by at least one half, although the demand for various materials will rise unevenly, in some cases going up as little as a quarter, in others rising fourfold or more. For instance, it is estimated that by the year 1975 the demand for minerals, as a whole, will increase by 90 per cent, for timber products by 10 per cent, for agricultural products by about 40 per cent, while the needs for total energy will double and those for water for industrial use alone will almost triple.

As to our over-all position, it is recognized that our dependency on the rest of the world will increase considerably and that we shall have to look to other countries for about one fifth of everything, other than food and gold, that we shall require. As a consequence our production deficit will be double or more what it is today.

There is one disarmingly direct observation that appears in the report. It is made simply and bluntly but gives one the feeling that it is partly prophetic in its implication. It is: "The United States appetite for materials is Gargantuan — and so far, insatiable." *So far*. What meaning for the future may be hidden in those two brief words. We Americans are too deeply involved in the expanding processes of our vital, headlong enterprise to pause and wonder. Why should we? Let's keep going!

And yet no one would deny the need to look into the future. There is yet another observation in the commission's report that is astounding. By drawing attention to what has happened in the past it compels attention to what may lie ahead. It states: "*The quantity of most metals and mineral fuels used in the United States since the first World War exceeds the total used throughout the entire world in all of history preceding 1914.*" It is difficult to absorb the thought that we Americans have used as much of the earth's riches in forty years as all people, the world over, have used in four thousand! Quite a record — but can we go on like that? This, of course, is the big question.

One of the thoughts suggested by this situation is that the United States is now beginning to face circumstances that bear at least some resemblance to those that have so seriously affected Great Britain and a number of European countries. Their colonial empires served not merely a political but largely an economic purpose, and once the flow of resources was checked, the whole concept of "colony" became meaningless. Vast as are the natural physical endowments of the United States, the fact is that its economy is outgrowing its resource base. It is no accident, therefore, that the United States in recent decades has been creating "economic colonies" in other countries — in its case not through the medium of government action but through the expansionist activities of industrial corporations. Within the last four or five years a few American companies have met with the "Get Out" sign from other countries, written as clearly as that of "Finis" to the colonial ties of such countries as Great Britain or Holland.

Are these incidents passing and unlikely to recur, or do they indeed represent an omen of things to come? Can our country, in effect, count upon continuing to get from other countries the raw materials it must have to sustain its economy? We could make no greater error than assuming this as a foregone conclusion. Our chances are not improved by the fact that populations are increasing so rapidly all over the world. At present rates of increase, there will be a billion more people on the earth at the century's end. This population pressure is a principal cause of intensified nationalism, which tends to culminate in one country after another saying, "We intend to keep our own land and resources for our own needs." Thus the episodes of current history are not surprising: the failure of the British oil negotiations in Iran, the expulsion of the Dutch from the East Indies, the exclusion of foreign interests in the Argentine. Even the savage action of the Mau Mau in Kenya, Africa, must be recognized, whether we like it or not, as a symptom of the times.

No easy prospect faces us. As suggested in the preceding chapter, we have entered an era when new conceptions regarding the ownership and use of natural resources must be adopted. Traditional ideas are not good enough, if for no other reason than that they will not work. Our best, if not our only chance, lies in the encouragement of economic interdependence between ourselves and all other countries in the free world. This will call for daring and enlightened action and will require sacrifices by individual interests in the matter of modifying protective tariffs and even on the part of all our people in not seeking ever-higher standards of living. We had better make some sacrifices earlier than

have little left later. We are increasingly, through political and social action, recognizing the values of the
share-and-share-alike concept at home. Now, whether
we will it or no, forces largely of our own making will
require that we apply this concept in our dealings with
other peoples.

No people can afford to do less than contemplate,
attempt to understand and try to make plans suitable
to the probabilities of the future. This we are not sufficiently endeavoring to do, and, like many other countries before us, appear to be assuming that we can
muddle through somehow. So far we have been fortunate and have succeeded in what a British historian
has lately termed "the western miracle of combining
a phenomenal increase of population with rising standards of living." If he is correct in his selection of the
term "miracle," how long can we in the United States
be expected to continue to perform one? We, in self-
confidence based on performance so far, may say, "Oh,
indefinitely — count on us!" From a scientific and technological point of view there appear, for the moment,
to be no visible limits to progress, even though we may
not be too clear in our minds as to what "progress" is
and where it may lead us. From a cultural and social
point of view there must be a saturation point, where
the human being, with the ancient prayer still in his
heart — "Lead us beside the still waters" — has reached
his limit of acceptance of the so-called "benefits" that

progress thrusts upon him. Could it be that we are approaching that point now?

These interrogations will be dismissed by many on the grounds that the only reliable gauge of progress in the modern world is that recorded by the barometer of business and trade. This is a satisfying and comforting viewpoint when things are going well and the miracle continues. But, even the most ardent advocate of the materialistic school dares not believe that the American standard of living is going to advance indefinitely. The signs are about us that we are approaching a turning point — the same point around which other nations, both contemporary and ancient, have revolved — some to survive, others to disappear. The day is here when we Americans need to clarify what we mean by a "standard of living" and in so doing give greater recognition to the immeasurable values of social, and not merely economic, criteria. We may dismiss Thoreau, who preached restriction of wants instead of increase in material goods — but we cannot forget him. As time goes on we may be compelled to take at least a portion of his philosophy as our own — even though it is not of our choice.

Neither the theories of economists nor the skills of industry and technology permit a disregard of the danger signals. It would be better, in a way, if the difficulties we are approaching were more apparent and a few at least were so dramatic and acute as to create general public awareness and compel action early rather than late. The episode in the spring of the year 1935, when the sun was darkened from the Rocky Mountains to the Atlantic by vast clouds of soil particles borne from the denuded grasslands of the Western states, jolted our people into action and gave birth to a conservation movement that is now well begun though as yet far from adequate. We may hear dimly, like a navigator at sea, the low and distant warning from another vessel, but we persuade ourselves that she is horizon-distant and bearing another course. There are as yet no scarlet flashes on our roadway to the future, and should these appear we would assure ourselves the road is broad and the accident somebody else's. Great Britain and Europe's difficulties are not ours, we pretend, and drive on. Nor is that of other peoples, past or present; they are different, we say — and drive on. Yes, our situation is different — every country's situation is different — one from the other. But we, too, are under the control of the eternal equation — the relationship between our resources and the numbers as well as the needs of our people.

V. AFRICA

To whom will it belong?

N<small>OT SO LONG AGO</small> our earth-home seemed boundless, as in the daydream of a child. Even Magellan and those other first explorers surely sensed infinity — their ships far from harbor and no land ahead. Within the century the last elusive "lost horizon" has gone forever. The questing spirit of man may conjure with outer space to feed his agelong yearning for still another unknown destination, thus reliving the fable of Icarus. If, unlike in the fable, the adventurer should return unharmed, it would be to live out his days on his own planet, that has now become so finite and so small.

We people, of whatever land, still speak of "far places." But we realize they are not really so — a journey between two dawns and darks will bring us to any of them. No longer, too, are these places "strange" in the sense of unknown. A great deal is known, although much is still to be learned. Even a half century ago it would have been impossible to write the descriptions which follow regarding Africa and the Amazon. In this relatively brief interval of time hosts of geogra-

phers, geologists, agronomists, explorers, traders, indus-
trialists, physicists, natural scientists, missionaries, medical people, government people and just plain travelers,
eliminating distance by airplane or automobile, have
amassed volumes of information regarding these two
vast regions.

Consequently it is possible to consider them, with
at least some degree of accuracy, in the light of this discussion of the world problem of peoples and their resources.

Like any continent, Africa is complex and diverse
in its geography and political structure as well as varied
in its resources. Therefore, in drafting even the broad
outlines of the relationships between food supplies and
populations of this major portion of the earth's surface,
one runs the risk of omitting details that in themselves
may be of real importance.

At first glance Africa is a study in contradictions.
While its people, as a whole, have a diet that is far
from adequate, this continent, second only to Asia in
the vastness of its territory, is at the same time a major
exporter of vegetable oils, a minor exporter of cereals,
and the source of two thirds of the world's cacao. With
scarcely any metal industries of its own, it provides cop-
per, manganese, chrome, tin, lead, zinc, iron and cobalt
to the industrial markets of Europe and North America.
The Belgian Congo's Shinkolobwe mine is at the present time the world's largest producer of high-grade

uranium ore, and constitutes one of the principal sources of the United States supply. Although innumerable people in the northern or southern regions are unable to clothe themselves adequately, Africans export cotton, wool and hides. While the crying need of most of the continent's subsistence farmers is for phosphate fertilizer to fortify their impoverished soils, Morocco and Tunisia in North Africa supply nearly one fourth of all the phosphate rock used elsewhere in the world. The majority of Africans are without the means to buy many of their vital needs, particularly nourishing foods for themselves and mineral fertilizers for their lands, although the mines of their continent yield over 40 per cent of the world's new gold and about 97 per cent of its industrial and gem diamonds.

Why these contrasts? Why these apparent inconsistencies? A brief analysis of this great continent and its people may clarify at least some of them. In its physical structure, Africa is the simplest of all the continents. Yet the character of that simplicity has been the greatest natural obstacle to its economic integration and development. The whole of its interior from Tunisia to the Cape of Good Hope is, in the main, a plateau possessing a few intermountain basins and several towering mountain ranges. The continent, except in parts of the West African littoral, rises almost abruptly from the ocean depths, with only narrow or arid coastal plains, sometimes none at all, to mark the cleavage between land and sea along its rim. Its great rivers, the Nile, Congo, Zambezi, Niger and the Orange, are blocked by falls and rapids relatively so close to their mouths they offer no easy avenues of penetration to the interior such as are provided by the Mississippi and the Amazon. The rugged topography of Africa, aside from impeding intercourse with the outside world, has accentuated the difficulties of interregional overland trade, which is also handicapped by the overseas orientation of major commercial activities. The colonial status of most African states plus the nature of the terrain have divided rather than integrated the continent. Commercial surpluses produced in certain areas have tended to flow abroad rather than into the deficit regions. Frequently this condition prevails within a single colony or independent state. Politically Africa presents the greatest diversity, with the most disturbing conditions existing at the three corners of its land mass: in the northwest, in the northeast and at the southern tip.

In this age of hydroelectric energy the plateau character of Africa could become an advantage. The cataracts over which fluvial waters cascade on their journeys to the sea represent over two fifths of the entire world's potential water power — four times as much as all North America's potential. Yet only $\frac{1}{10}$ of 1 per cent is utilized! What differences in the productivity of African soils might a small portion of this energy create if harnessed for the manufacture of nitrogen fertilizers? The sites for the generation of power, so few of which are as yet put to use, have until the past century served to seal off the heart of Africa from inquisitive explorers and commercial adventurers, who feared to travel overland through forests or deserts and who could not, of course, make their way by ships. Thus it was that Africa, whose Mediterranean coast and lower Nile Valley have been known since the beginning of recorded time, remained one of the truly hidden parts of the world until the latter half of the nineteenth century.

One fifth of all the world's land surface lies within the bounds of Africa. To be sure, almost one third of this continent is composed of deserts, which all together are as large as the United States, India, Mexico and Alaska. Yet much of this arid expanse is suitable, to some degree, for grazing livestock. Scarcely 8 per cent of Africa is so dry as to be entirely useless to man or beast. Even the great Sahara is more sparse shrub and scattered grass than bare, shifting dunes or windswept gravel surfaces. Very dry though they may be, the deserts of the north and southwest portions of Africa are of subsistence value to small populations of nomadic herdsmen living by their flocks of goats, sheep and their less common herds of cattle. Under the present methods of management there is little prospect that these lands, now occupied by fewer than two persons per square mile, could support more livestock or more people than they do today. A limited amount of irrigation is feasible and rotational grazing of the grasslands would improve their capacity to carry more livestock.

For centuries desert nomads have been the hardiest warriors of Africa, stark necessity forcing them to challenge the encroachment of other peoples upon their domain because the lands would not support an added burden. Rainfall in the thin grass and thornbush regions seldom exceeds twenty inches annually; more frequently it is less than ten inches. In this type of country there are widespread conditions of overgrazing and wind-eroded soils. Such light precipitation, coupled with high temperatures, has been insufficient to promote good grass cover, especially since well-managed rotational grazing is almost unknown. The herded animals tend to suppress the grass by overgrazing, thus allowing the encroachment of less desirable thornwood. Ranchers in the semiarid prairies of Texas have seen mesquite invade their properties in the same way for the same reasons.

Only in exceptional and limited places, where rivers cross the deserts or ground water is available, may new, irrigated agricultural lands be developed through the aid of modern engineering. The Gezira district in the fork above the junction of the White and Blue Nile rivers is a good example of such development. Much of this region's potential is already under cultivation as the result of a modern venture in African land reclamation. Yet let us draw the picture of Africa's irrigated acres in proper perspective. All the oases of the continent, including the fertile Nile Valley, scarcely amount to ⅒ of 1 per cent of its area. Egypt is about as large as Texas and New Mexico combined; yet its people must sustain themselves on 9500 square miles irrigated by the Nile — an area only slightly larger than the State of Vermont for over twenty million people! No wonder it is in political turmoil, although this is not the only reason, to be sure.

More than anything else, Africa is a grassland world with but comparatively small truly forested regions. In addition to desert shrubs and grasses covering almost half the continent, another large proportion of the continent, approximately two fifths, is dominated either by prairies or parks of grass and trees. Never does tree growth in these parks become so dense as to shade out grasses beneath the trees. The American botanist H. L. Shantz, after years of travel and study of the flora of Africa, observed that even in what he calls the "dry forests," it is generally possible to see for distances of up to half a mile beneath the thin canopy of broad-topped trees, which never succeed either in closing out the sunlight or in stifling the grasses. Fires set by native herdsmen burn through the park savannas — a very ancient practice by which primitive man has thinned out the woody growth to favor the forage which his domestic livestock and the great herds of wildlife prefer. One of the serious impediments to the fuller use of much of the park-savanna country is the tsetse fly, which spreads the nagana disease, commonly called "sleeping sickness" and affecting both man and livestock. Continued research may eventually provide some means of immunization against nagana, thus extending the areas of usable range, which indeed contain the potentiality of becoming one of the great grazing regions of the world.

Today this environment is satisfactory for small scattered human populations subsisting upon hoe agriculture, and, where the tsetse is not a menace, for animal husbandry. Rainfall is generally sufficient during six months of the year for a great variety of food crops to be raised, including corn, sorghums, manioc, sweet potatoes, yams, beans and peanuts. In parts of the Congo Basin, on the outer margins of the true rain forest, annual precipitation may reach seventy-five inches and in exceptional cases as much as a hundred. There the oil palm, cassava, bananas, pineapples, citrus fruits, rice and sugar cane can be grown successfully.

Part of the task of the future is to assess the capacity of Africa — of its soils, its climates, and its various peoples — for producing more food and fiber, as well as to study to what degree Africa can make room for those who find themselves unable to gain employment or a decent livelihood in overcrowded countries.

Obviously Africa can be counted on to supplement the food supplies of Europe or other parts of the world. Whether Africa can be relied upon to feed and clothe the Africans adequately, or any substantial number of foreign peoples who might emigrate there, is quite another matter. This question is one which has so impressed the Belgian government, for example, that its program for the development of the Congo calls for rigid restriction of European immigration except by special arrangement. The eminent tropical-soil scientist Robert L. Pendleton, writing of his travels in the Congo in 1948 and 1949, mentions that one of the outstanding colonization schemes, the Congo Belge Katanga, accepted only ten Belgian families in 1948 and expected to accept fifteen in 1949 and twenty in 1950. He explained that the government is determined to prevent the growth of a poor white community. Also it realizes that each colonist will, in all likelihood, become a landed proprietor and an employer of Negro labor. The authorities are reluctant to allow such newcomers to compete for a limited labor supply, since already some seven hundred thousand natives out of a total population of about eleven million are employed in the Congo mines and the palm and rubber plantations of Europeans.

Problems such as the above face not only the Congo but all highland Africa which is under European administration. From the beginning of white settlement on that continent the native peoples have gradually been obliged to alter their methods of land utilization and their own individual and tribal ways of living to suit the commercial needs of the newcomers. The white man has arrived as a miner and a planter of commercial export crops; yet he has not come to do the manual work himself. Both mines and plantations demand quantities of man power which in the past the Africans devoted to raising their own subsistence crops and livestock, almost to the complete exclusion of what they might sell abroad. That poor whites of European stock, however desperate, will not accept the wages and living standards of the African common laborer has already been amply demonstrated with socially disastrous consequences in the Union of South Africa, to which reference will be made in subsequent pages.

Among the exceptions to the white planter dominance of African commercial agriculture in the colonial states is the cacao industry of the Gold Coast and Nigeria, which is in the hands of the indigenous peoples, who, as small-scale family operators, produce almost the entire crop. Like the Belgians, the British have also recognized the wisdom of excluding white settlement in their West African colonies, where land ownership is reserved for Africans. Recent desires to restrain the migration of whites from the Union of South Africa into Nyasaland and the Rhodesias indicate an extension of this policy.

Not all the soils of humid and subhumid Africa are suitable for agriculture, even of the subsistence type, for it is a fairly common observation that the native is most exacting in his selection of planting sites. Part of this caution is due to poor soils being more common than good ones and part, no doubt, to the realization that steep, deforested slopes are as great a menace as poor soils. In the zones of heavy precipitation the most essential elements of plant nutrition have been all but completely leached away from the mineral portions of the ground. What fertility may be readily available is chiefly stored in accumulations of humus. Under cultivation humus rapidly decomposes, releasing its elements to the growing crops, enabling them to maintain good yields for two or three years — until the humus is exhausted. Then most lands must be abandoned and new clearings made on virgin ground. Dr. Charles E. Kellogg, chief of the United States Soil Survey Division, after a study of the African tropics, reported to the International Congress of Soil Science at Amsterdam in 1950 that, generalizing very broadly, the only soils of the humid tropics which are naturally relatively productive are those which have been rejuvenated through additions of volcanic ash, rich alluvial deposits, or where natural erosion has been active enough to expose to root penetration comparatively unweathered mineral materials rich in plant nutrients. Such soils are as scarce in Africa as in most other large, humid, tropical areas of the earth. Dr. Kellogg went on, however, to explain that many poor soils can often be improved by wise management involving the application of modern scientific knowledge. As yet, Africa has only scratched the surface of what might be learned through modern scientific research.

Over much of the more humid tropical parklands the processes of soil formation have resulted in an accumulation of ironstone lenses, or laterite, a substance suitable for building blocks or road surfacing but scarcely for agriculture. How extensively laterite occurs no one knows, but it is recognized by soil scientists as being one of the urgent reasons for making detailed soil surveys before hazarding predictions as to Africa's agricultural potential. Laterite is also a problem in true rain-forest sections of the Congo and West Africa. There again we must wait for good soil maps to tell us whether it is of major or minor significance. French, British and Belgian scientists have all noted extensive areas of it in their respective colonies. Laterite is commonly encountered in the soils of other humid tropical portions of the world in the Amazon Valley, India, and southeast Asia. Everywhere it is the same story — where there is laterite the land is generally unsuited either for subsistence or commercial crops.

In the zones of parks and prairies, where rainfall may be between twenty and forty inches annually, the native Africans have equally important although different reasons for caution in selecting planting sites. They are quite aware that sands and some clays may be almost worthless in dry years, for they are so permeable they hold little moisture in reserve. To farmers in the temperate zones it might seem strange to hear of clays which behave like sands; yet that is a normal characteristic of *latosol* clays, the most common of all tropical clay types. The best sites the native planters have found in moisture-critical areas are those with high water tables, where underground reserves may supplement rainfall in times of drought. Such preferable locations are comparatively limited.

It is rather typical of the climate in the drier park and prairie zones that rainfall is erratic in frequency. There are times when the rains fail to arrive when needed most for plant growth. Subsistence cultivators have ways of avoiding these risks but their methods would hardly be considered economical on a commercial scale. The natives avoid monoculture, or single crop systems, so typical of commercial agriculture. They interplant varieties of crops on the same pieces of ground, seeding them at different times during the growing season. Thus they are almost certain that a portion of what they plant will respond favorably regardless of when the rains fall. Hand and hoe tillage permit this whereas it is seldom feasible with machinery. What is lost by drought, if it comes, is not their entire planting. Then, too, if there were more mixed farming, livestock could eke out an existence whether the grass was green or dry.

A failure to appreciate the reasons for the African's caution in choosing tillable lands in the park and prairie regions led to the crippling of one of the most colossal agricultural development schemes of modern times — the East African peanut project fostered by the British government shortly after World War II. Britain was extremely short of vegetable oils for her own people. It was envisioned that 3,000,000 acres of peanuts could be established in the lands of Tanganyika, Northern Rhodesia and Kenya. The plan called for a dramatic invasion by thousands of tractors and bulldozers together with an army of 30,000 African laborers and 750 British technicians. In its conception the scheme called for new railways, immense storage facilities, and extensive port installations to accommodate ocean freighters which would bring in machinery and haul away peanuts. Hospitals, schools, roads, fertilizer stockpiles, housing projects, and public water systems were all envisaged and undertaken to realize the dream. Scarcely anything was overlooked except the vital factors of soils and climate, as well as the working habits of the Africans. To be sure, the government was advised to experiment before plunging, but this note of caution was disregarded in the excitement of attacking the earth as though it were a military objective. The results were catastrophic. Soils which felt like loams to technicians from temperate Britain turned out to be clays, friable and workable when moist, but hard as stone when dry. Such meager precipitation records as were obtainable indicated adequate amounts, but the vagaries of African rainfall did not show up in the statistics. In some places droughts came at critical periods and harvesttime found surviving plants with their nuts encased in a clay armor which stripped the vines of their fruit as they were pulled from the earth by mechanical diggers.

The shock and disappointment that followed the collapse of such ambitious hopes were due not only to the large amount of money that was lost and the frustrations and wasted physical effort of both the British and the Africans. The really crushing blow was to an idea which offered a prospect that not only would Britain be better fed by the yields of the African earth but the native diets would be improved as well. The idea was that abundance for both could only be achieved by changing the agricultural techniques of the African — to put the tractor in his hands instead of the hoe, for with the hoe he could not hope to cultivate more ground than necessary to feed himself. With tractors, adequate fertilizers and the advice of agronomists and soil conservationists, it was hoped each African could multiply the fruits of his labor. The scheme did not call for separating the native from his land and turning it over to European colonists to act as employers of Negro workmen. It was planned as a co-operative enterprise, with the native communities providing land and labor and with Britain supplying capital investments and technical personnel. The profits were to be shared by the African tiller and his local governments — truly an auspicious concept in colonial administration. It must be added that the idea has not been entirely abandoned. A new effort is under way on a much reduced scale, with good prospects — after the lessons so bitterly learned — of achieving sizable results.

Some such approach as that of the peanut project would seem essential if European colonial powers in Africa are not to suffer the same nationalist revolts which in the nineteenth century drove them from all but the fringes of the American tropics and which in this century have obliged them to withdraw from India and Indonesia and which threaten their expulsion from the Near East. Britain, France and Belgium each realizes how severe the economic consequences would be at home if they could no longer draw upon Africa's raw materials. In this realization lies the hope of a wiser use of land and human resources on that continent, but the ways in which this more enlightened approach are to be expressed will call for the most careful examinations not only of African soils and climates but of political and economic policies as well.

As yet we have not considered "Darkest Africa" — the tropical rain forests of the Congo, the Cameroons, and the Guinea Coast. Much as these places have captured our imagination, they are but a small portion of the continent — approximately 14 per cent. Most of the upland soils are severely weathered and leached of minerals essential to crops. Before European occupation, and even up to the present, where land regulations of colonial administrations permit, the natives practice a system of shifting cultivation similar to that practiced by the Amazonians on their upland soils. Forests are cut and the trash burned during a dry season. Crops of manioc, corn, rice, yams, beans, and sweet potatoes are grown for a few years, until the humus is destroyed; then they are abandoned and gradually the forest reclaims the clearings. This type of agriculture is possible as long as land resources greatly exceed the immediate needs of the cultivators. Such a cropping system is in effect a true rotation in which the forest occupies the ground most of the time and man's food crops only a fraction of it. It involves heavy expenditures of human effort and would be impractical commercially. When only the food supply of the tillers and their families is involved and they have no other obligations to fulfill or ambitions to appease, they can manage, as indeed they have for centuries past. These tillage methods are a survival of the days before European settlement when all the lands of Central Africa belonged to the tribes, as they still do in some places. Such a system of shifting cultivation recognizes no need for private land ownership since permanent land improvement for subsistence cropping is itself undesirable — although community land ownership does exist in many tribal districts. In the past the problem of possessing sufficient territory upon which to shift freely was a tribal concern — the individual, if he helped the tribe defend its realm, was granted the use of all the land he needed, and use was the important thing.

Needless to say, the manner of existence enjoyed by Congo and Guinea Coast tribesmen would scarcely appeal to a European refugee. Neither would such a system of agriculture produce abundant surpluses for a European market. The most successful commercial enterprises in the rain-forest portions of Africa have been plantations of tree crops: cacao, oil, palm and rubber. Soil productivity is maintained because the ground is not disturbed and leaf litter from the trees replenishes the humus supply just as in natural palm and hardwood forests. The successful introduction of commercial tree crops into the rain-forest areas of Liberia, the Gold Coast, Nigeria and the Congo meant also the introduction of the idea of individual land ownership since tree crops require permanent land improvements and constant care. British policy in Nigeria and the Gold Coast fostered cultivation by Africans of individual plots of ground, where they devoted themselves to cacao and oil palms. In Liberia, American capital has set up land-development corporations employing native labor. In the Congo the usual practice has been to grant large holdings to corporations or to a few selected Belgian colonists, who in turn hire Negro workmen.

As a result of these shifts in land use, the areas of tribal territories have shrunk, while tribal populations have often increased relative to the size of their holdings. The effect has been felt not only in the rainforest regions but also in those park savanna and prairie zones where European settlers have been admitted and given lands for the cultivation of export crops. Taxes have often been imposed upon the African with the consequence that he has had to produce more export crops or seek work elsewhere, in mines or plantations, in order to pay them. Where native reserves have been established, they have frequently proved insufficient to support the tribes. For a while they graze and cultivate their lands excessively, until declining yields and soil erosion force them to work for cash wages to support their families. In the Congo whole villages have been obliged to move into settlements most accessible to tax collectors. The result, apart from its questionable social consequences, has too frequently been abusive overexploitation of the land, soil erosion, declining yields and poorer diets for the natives. To be sure, export crops are obtained.

A 1946 report of the United Nations Food and Agriculture Organization summarized the per capita food consumption of various countries previous to World War II. It showed that the diets in the following African territories were below the minimum standard for proper nutrition — Morocco, Tunisia, Algeria, West Africa, Kenya, Uganda and the Union of South Africa. Recent plans of the French government for its African dependencies anticipate raising the nutritional level of indigenous peoples to between 2000 and 2500 calories per capita per day. The average for France itself is approximately 3000. We in the United States consume more than 3200 calories per person daily. The very minimum for decent health, even in the tropics, is considered to be above 2500. Prewar France enjoyed an average of thirteen pounds of fat and oil per person annually while the people of her West African colonies, who were furnishing part of the palm and peanut oils to make this possible, were subsisting on six pounds. Postwar plans call for more than tripling the vegetable-oil output of French West African territories to a goal of 940,000 tons, of which it is expected 880,000 tons will be exported and 60,000 left for local consumption. Will the nutritional levels of France's 42,000,000 people be maintained at the cost of malnutrition among nearly an identical number of Africans who send her not surpluses, but food they need themselves? Or, is it possible that modern techniques will be developed in Africa for African conditions so that enough will be available for the rapidly increasing populations of Africa as well? The answer is still to be found.

A hundred years ago the population of Africa was about a hundred million. No reliable knowledge exists as to the continent's population in earlier times, although such scholars as A. M. Carr-Saunders and W. F. Willcox have deduced that previous figures were not higher, and there is some evidence that around the year 1800 the continent's numbers were somewhat below a hundred million. Now, according to the latest censuses and estimates of the United Nations, the total approximates two hundred million, or double the figure of a century ago. At an increase rate of 1 per cent a year for sixty-nine years a population will double its numbers. If the rate of increase is 2 per cent annually it will take thirty-five years to double. If the annual rate of increase is 3 per cent it will take but twenty-three years to achieve the same results. According to present indications, or, more accurately, if today's estimated rates of increase should be maintained, the population of Africa would double within the next fifty or sixty years — meaning another two hundred million people to be provided for — and its present population is food-short!

Scientific public health control of epidemic diseases is drastically cutting down mortality rates which formerly almost matched births in the undeveloped regions of the earth. Is Africa prepared or can she become prepared to meet the weight of increasing human numbers? Who can positively predict? It is quite apparent, however, that by hoe tillage the African cannot support himself properly and satisfy Europe's own increasing demands. There is indication in the rates of capital investment in colonial development projects at the present time that it will be possible for a while. Since World War II almost every African colony or mandate has received imports either equal in value to or in excess of the value of its exports. This is accounted for to a considerable degree by imports of capital equipment sent to Africa by the mother countries. This is a good sign but it is not enough.

In a primitive agricultural or pastoral society little children of six or seven years work alongside their fathers and mothers. Modern methods of husbandry and industry afford no place for such child labor. Large families then become a burden rather than an asset. Failure to appreciate this condition in the former colonial territories of Asia and America led to a temporary increase of exports to Europe until native populations had grown to the point where stark hunger, among other causes, drove them to rebellion. Africa is still one of the least populated of the continents in terms of its potential in arable lands and livestock ranges, but it cannot be expected to retain this advantage long unless crop yields and labor efficiency both begin to increase at a rate faster than the population multiplies. The great hope for the future is that enlightened colonial policies, including capital investment and technical progress, may result in the native peoples' arriving at such an improved educational and economic level that they will voluntarily recognize that well-being and constant increases in numbers cannot go hand in hand.

Too few Western nations have yet grasped the idea that it won't be sufficient simply to increase the productivity of the African — he must share, to a truly reasonable extent, the benefits that modern technology is capable of bringing to him. Readiness to grant him an ample proportion of whatever progress is made in his own country is the only attitude that can lead to an orderly development of this vast region through the combined efforts of native peoples and those of the Western world. Otherwise, one can even now sense the outcome, because the first faint words regarding it are already being written on the books of future time. They read: *The African will take his land for his own.*

VI. SOUTH AFRICA

*A land dissolving
in the acids of conflict*

THE HISTORIES of peoples in relation to their
lands contain many variables. Customs and cultures,
whether social or religious, profoundly affect the attitude of peoples toward the environments in which
they live. Good practices are not the monopoly of any
one people. The farmer of Japan or Ceylon is as competent, in his own way, as the farmer of northern Europe. By contrast, the cattle or sheep owner whose herds
overgraze a range in Wyoming is the true successor of
the herdsman whose flocks nipped the last grasses from
the hills of Lebanon. Custom, attitude and method are
of the essence today as they have been in earlier times.
The relics of forms of land-ownership, such as the
latifundia, which during two thousand years were
transferred from Rome to Spain and presently exist in
much of Latin America, are disadvantages inherited
from the past. Religious concepts are both favorable
and unfavorable — as illustrated by the excellence of
land usage practiced by the Mennonites in Pennsyl-
vania and the harm resulting from the sacredness of

the cow in India. Progress in meeting the present world need for agricultural improvement and reform will be measured by the degree to which the unfavorable inheritances from the past can be eliminated. Similarly, any computations as to increases to be scored by agriculture in world food production are unrealistic if these cultural and social impediments are disregarded or it is assumed that those that are unfavorable can be easily or rapidly overcome.

In this connection, South Africa is an interesting case study. One should not generalize too much from what has happened there because its story of land and people is in many respects unique. The region itself runs to extremes both as to the wealth and contrasting scarcity of its natural resources. These extremes have had far-reaching social consequences. One of the most curious things about this land is the influence it has had upon the people of entirely different origins that have come to it, especially the metamorphosis it has worked upon the early colonists from Holland. But beyond all this, South Africa is a country that exemplifies the obstacles resulting from old prejudices and traditions that stand in the way of progress.

"This Cape is a most stately thing and the fairest Cape we saw in the whole circumference of the Earth," wrote Sir Francis Drake of his first view of the Cape of Good Hope in the year 1580. The keen eyes of the navigator were looking towards another mysterious region among the many he had viewed during his three-year voyage. It was not his mission to leave his ship the *Golden Hind* and explore the country that lay beyond the distant sky line. He could not guess that within those farthest hills lay hidden stores of gold and diamonds that later were to draw his own people to this land and eventually to make of it a Dominion within the British-Commonwealth-to-be. He could not foresee what lay in store for the different races of men who were to meet there and make this country their home, nor could he ever have imagined the assault that man was to make upon the virgin land itself.

The Union is the only independent state in Africa that is controlled by the descendants of settlers from European nations, although Southern Rhodesia is now approaching that condition. Two and one half million white people of European origin, approximately one half of the continent's total, live there. Two thirds of these are Afrikaaners, or Boers, originally Dutch, with three hundred years of history in South Africa behind them. They have their own language, Afrikaans. The remaining third have English forebears, some dating back as long as one hundred and fifty years. Generations of occupancy and achievement give both groups rights to their land. But while the English-speaking people still have feelings of kinship with their original countries, most Afrikaaners have become exclusively and intensely nationalistic.

103

In addition to these Europeans, there are over nine million African natives, about one million of whom have intermarried with other races. The rest of the population consists of a quarter of a million Asiatics, mostly descendants of imported Indian laborers.

These twelve million inhabitants of the Union of South Africa live not so much with as among each other. There is suspicion and lack of friendliness between white and nonwhite generally, between Afrikaaners and English-speaking whites, between Afrikaaner-controlled agriculture and British-controlled industry, and between all of these and the Asiatics.

South Africa is not the land of wide-open spaces, as is sometimes thought. It has large modern cities, with skyscrapers, luxury shops and slums. Its natives are poorly fed farm and industrial workers. Except in the sanctuaries of its splendid national park system, its once rich heritage of wild animal life has virtually disappeared.

Rapidly becoming industrialized and urbanized, the Union is the richest gold and diamond country in the world. Exclusive of gold exports, it accounts for 25 per cent of the total African merchandise foreign trade and for about 40 per cent of the intra-African trade. It has the only significant iron and steel plant on the continent. In many ways it is a modern, thriving community.

But there are serious economic, political and cultural problems in the Union. Intricately and inevitably involved with them is the imbalance of the relationship between the people and their natural resources. Each year there are two hundred thousand more people in the Union, and as each year passes it becomes more and more doubtful whether the productivity of the land is even holding its own.

As recently as 1920 the Union's population stood at about five million. In slightly more than a single generation, a mere thirty years, it has more than doubled, with no end to increasing numbers yet in sight. With the extension of medical services, resulting in decreased infant mortality and the lowering of the death rate, has come this mounting population pressure. At the same time, traditional mores keep the birth rate high. While there is a high percentage of malnutrition and chronic disease among the natives, whole populations are no longer virtually exterminated by plagues, as were the Hottentots during the 1713 smallpox epidemic.

By nature the land of South Africa is relatively low in fertility. Much of the country is semiarid and the few rivers are mostly seasonal and spaced far apart. Agricultural conditions, at best, were not originally favorable, and the effects of long years of improper farming make reclamation doubly difficult. Many areas, more suitable for grazing than for crops, have been so seriously overstocked that there has been wholesale depletion of the natural herbage. Following upon this, heavy seasonal rainfalls have led to soil erosion on so widespread a scale that the very character of the country's water supplies are being changed. The oft-quoted remark of the late premier, Jan Smuts, that "erosion is the biggest problem facing the country — bigger than any politics" was not made carelessly. While in some areas there has been an improvement, it is doubtful whether South Africa can ever be self-sufficient in regard to food.

Some explanation of the present disparity between the population and its resources can be given by examining the past. The development of South Africa has been marred by inherited racial conflicts. It is a story of climate, soil, gold, slavery, superstition. Especially it is the story of the Boer, for in his development can be found many of the seeds of the country's present predicament.

The first Dutch settlers at the Cape, in 1652, had no real interest in Africa at all. Their function was to provide food and hospital care for those on their way to or from the resources of India. Except for some French refugees in 1688, there was almost no additional settlement during the next century. But the Dutch, with a high birth rate, expanded and were given land by the Dutch East India Company for farming along the Liesbeek River.

At the time of the initial settlement, there were substantial forests and an abundance of game, and

whales and seals were numerous in the bay. Commander van Riebeek, seemingly a pioneer wildlife conserva-
tionist, allowed only two of his men the privilege of
shooting wild game, although premiums were offered
for the destruction of lions, hyenas and leopards.

Van Riebeek desired a small, tightly knit, self-sufficient community with as few contacts as possible with
the native populations. But the Boers, as the descendants of the original settlers were called, gradually began to move farther and farther into the interior of
the Cape Colony. Much later on, the Great Trek, begun in 1836, was made as a protest against the British
emancipation of the slaves. The way of life of the trek
Boer, still an influence on the present South African
manner of thinking, stems from the very early days.

Various reasons are given to explain this phenome-
non of a large segment of population, not by origin
vagabonds or adventurers, becoming pioneers. As always, in new countries, there is the lure of the fron-
tier. Many Boers chafed under the regulations of the
Dutch East India Company, and it was easier to turn
away from restrictions than to face them. With new
lands available it was easier, too, to exhaust one farming or grazing area and then start another elsewhere
than to bother about careful land usage.

The pioneer may seek progress and freedom, or
merely a refuge from responsibilities. In the main the
Boer appeared to search for the latter. Courage was

necessary for the initial movements, but courage can prove somewhat of a variable, and it seems that the Boer, rather than attempt to establish a better society, sought to continue a narrower and more personal version of an older one.

For his actions the land itself was partly to blame. More suited for grazing than farming, it did not permit close settlement. Few villages developed, and large families in their large acreages were widely separated from each other. In an area of mild climate, rich game, and fresh lands beyond, intensive effort was not necessary. It was easy to forget the old Dutch habits of thrift and intensive cultivation. As the Boer appraised his needs, they were land and cattle, and both were available.

It is significant that while Americans and Australians found vast open spaces awaiting them, the Boer moved into lands in which there were already considerable native populations. Among these were the Bushmen, who ranged as nomads throughout the area. Very primitive, they lived on game, wild fruits and herbs. More powerful were the Hottentots, found along the western and southern coasts of the country. They did not cultivate crops, but lived on wild game and domestic cattle and sheep. The Bushmen could not long survive. The Hottentots — quickly subdued by the white man — and later the Bantu, became Africa's richest natural resource, a cheap labor force. This resource, together with slaves, profoundly affected the Boer outlook and way of life.

South African production and lack of intensive agriculture did not require slavery. Large numbers of workers were not needed, as they were, for example, in the West Indies, where slaves were a valuable property. Through shipping, the Cape had contact with the two great slave-trading coasts of the world, and with acquaintance had come a tolerance. Slavery rose out of an acceptance of the fact that slavery existed.

Van Riebeek had originally prohibited the taking of native lands and slavery. But by 1657, only five years after the original settlement, not only had the Hottentots been largely subdued, but slaves were imported from West Africa, East Africa, and Madagascar, as well as hundreds of Javanese coolies.

In a poor and unprosperous land, the presence of a surplus of ignorant natives and slaves became a means for attaining privilege and prestige rather than for general economic and social improvement. It soon became common practice that the natives should do the hard labor. Little was done to improve their lot, and their work, as a rule, was wasteful and inefficient. The population grew larger but not richer. As time went on the Boer came to think of manual labor as degrading. Since work was for natives, land became the goal for the young Afrikaaner. In this attitude we find another reason for Boer trekking.

On his farms, living separated from his white neighbors, the Boer lost the usual civilized sense of community. Like the American settler in the West, he had much of the courage and hardiness of the pioneer. He enjoyed the wide spaces, the slow movement of his life, and the lack of complication developing through change. An old-fashioned family man, he was stern, aloof and religious. Cut off from the Cape, he did not hear of new theories and ideas. The Bible was his only literature, and he found parallels between himself and the wanderings of the chosen people in the wilderness.

For the natives, however, there was no place in the Bible. At once Van Riebeek had called them "black stinking dogs." Considered pagans and savages, they had no place with humanity except as servants. The Boer farmer considered that the separation and degradation of the natives was ordained by God, and an uncompromising Calvinist church preached and endorsed this point of view.

On the veld, the difference between riches and poverty was not easily distinguishable. Lands and flocks were the measure, and they were readily obtainable. As long as there was sufficient land, there was little inducement to improve it. If the soil was used up or eroded, it mattered little. Even the exact area of a property was vague and not subject to control. Government and authority were so undefined and ineffectual that considerable lawlessness prevailed. But surrounded by his children, land, herds and natives, sustained by his Bible, the Boer felt a sense of special destiny. He was an individual and he wanted freedom, but freedom for himself alone — freedom from society, from efficient government, from culture, science and thought. Deep into the nineteenth century the Boers carried their earlier ways of life — attitudes and habits of mind which were later profoundly to influence all South Africa.

As the Boers trekked northward, they were confronted by the Bantu tribes moving south. Alan Paton, the South African novelist, describes the Bantu in this manner:

> They were often physically magnificent, and masters of a fiercely barbaric song and dance. Their system of law and custom was intricate and notable, and their social organization was simple and efficient. Prostitution was unknown, offenses rare, and children were obedient and respectful to their elders. Religion was something quite different from our own; the Supreme Spirit was high and unapproachable, but one's ancestors were near and of powerful influence.

The Bantu moved like herds of wild game, drifting from place to place as their needs led them. Their agriculture was primitive and wasteful: they made use of soil as long as it was fertile, then burned out a new area for cultivation. They were a pastoral people, but cattle meant more to them than mere wealth. As with the Hindu, cattle were an integral part of the culture. Although there was no ban on the eating of beef, the African's cattle were primarily considered as marks of prestige and were used as payment in the marriage dowry.

Like the Boer, the Bantu way of life demanded wide expanses of grazing land. With both groups, animals and soil worked against each other — overstocked animals injuring the land, the ill-cared-for land unable to feed animals properly.

The big conflict between the Boers and the Bantu came toward the end of the eighteenth century. Both groups wanted water, land and grass, and the clash caused war among the tribes themselves and between the tribes and the Boer. Insufficient space caused diseases among the herds and starvation among the natives. Both groups had become so involved that whatever happened to one affected the other. Black and white were insolubly linked. They are still so today.

When, in 1795, an English force took the Cape Colony, it found a still primitive country with only one town worthy of the name, and five or six little villages. Most of the population was scattered over an immense area.

The British brought with them something of the progressive outside world — humanitarianism, evangelicalism, and the ideas of law and order. The slave trade was abolished in 1807 and slavery in 1834. British missionaries welcomed natives as brothers in Christ and began to educate them. Law was extended to the heathen. The new ways of the nineteenth century suddenly broke in.

The British policies were greeted by the Boer with feelings of injustice and outrage. In a poor and unproductive land, social and economic distinctions are more important than in a more prosperous one. Education brought questions to the minds of natives. Previously the natives had accepted without thought the rule of the white men who had taken the place of tribal leaders. Lawful practice and abolition of slavery upset the labor market. Resentment was felt especially on the farms and frontiers.

In 1813 Governor Sir John Craddock issued a proclamation intended to bring order to landholdings and obtain revenue for the government. In areas of little government and inadequate officials, a quitrent would be paid. It was the hope that through these measures responsibilities would be felt and the land would become more productive, for the effects of poor farming were already beginning to be felt.

But order was not the result. Many Boers, resenting the foreigner, resenting restrictions, resenting advice, embarked on the Great Trek. Regulation of land settlement and new attitudes toward the natives left deep grievances. On the trek, natives were pushed ever into narrower, poorer confines of land, both by the

Boer, who was fleeing, and by the British military, who thought that the only way to preserve order was by force of arms. Loss of land meant more exhausting use of soil and less space for grazing. Natives became more poorly fed or became squatters and laborers on white men's land, there to continue the bad land practices common to both groups. Though no doubt the British administration made mistakes, it did bring a new degree of order to the country. However, the Boer, through trekking and non-co-operation, remained dominant as a force.

As for the Bantu, they lost not only much of their land, but their entire way of life. It is impossible to guess what might have happened to the African if he had been permitted to develop without European influence. Of whatever value and however primitive, there was at least some rational structure to tribal life, a fair distribution of food and land, and protection and comfort for the individual. The British, the Boer, the missionary, the soldier — all began to break down the native mode of existence. Europeanization brought not liberation but servitude.

In 1857, during the struggles of Kafir War, a terrible example of the effect of superstition occurred. The natives were told by their prophets that the white man could be turned back by means of a great sacrifice: all their cattle and corn must be destroyed. It is estimated that as a result twenty-five thousand natives died; and many thousands more, the tribes broken, became laborers for the Europeans.

So even before the discovery of gold and diamonds, the present pattern of life of the natives — forced to leave overcrowded, unproductive areas for rural labor — had been established. When diamonds were found in Hope Town in 1867 and gold in 1884-1885 in the Transvaal, natives were recruited into urban labor as well.

Mining demanded skill, precision, science, and business organization — requirements strange and out of place to the conservative, still eighteenth-century Boer. His simple society was challenged by a complex industrial and commercial order and by the arrival of aggressive Europeans, mostly English, who wanted to make money from the mines. Many Boers reacted characteristically — they sold their diamond- and gold-laden lands and fled. Today the mines are owned largely by British absentee shareholders — another cause for resentment.

The British and Europeans who came to the mines did not constitute an immigration in the usual sense. Most of them were adventurers, men who preferred speculation and excitement to a regular job at home. Consequently, the population growth in the Union has not been caused by the kind of immigration that occurred in Canada or Australia. Lack of industrialization and of opportunities for agricultural development, together with the huge number of native laborers, discouraged entry of the type of energy and enterprise that went to those other parts of the British Empire. For instance, about 5000 British settlers in 1820 failed on the land and moved to towns. Later on others came — a group of 4300 laborers between 1844 and 1847, and 12,000 German and British between 1857 and 1862. However, the steady, steep increase of population in the Union has come mainly from the large families of the Boer and Bantu.

A wave of immigration did follow the beginning of mining, but an immigration from within — swarms of natives. The resident Europeans were quick to adopt one basic Boer attitude. They did not want to do the hard labor. They became supervisors, and even engineers and skilled labor had to be specially imported.

So important has gold become that it provides the livelihood of approximately half of the Union's population as well as a large proportion of the finances of the government. It has virtually monopolized whatever industrial development the country might otherwise have attained. An object for speculation and dependent for its value upon remote political and monetary influences, it could not and has not become the basis of a new economic order.

Today in the Union approximately one third of the African natives live in the reserves which have been set aside for them, one third work in industry and mining, and one third on European farms. By the Land Act of 1913, a law passed ostensibly to protect the natives, white men were prohibited from buying land in the reserves. Conversely, natives could not buy, rent or acquire land outside the reserves. There was at least a mathematical discrepancy in the fact that the white man's lands were ten times as large. In 1950, 13 per cent of the land was reserved for over nine million natives and 87 per cent for the two and a half million whites.

Despite the inadequacies of the reserves, life there is usually better for the native than on the outside. He suffers from overcrowding, poverty, eroded farm lands, malnutrition, and, sadly, some of the diseases introduced by the white man. But some sort of tribal structure still exists and he has a family life. Usually ignorant, he continues his old, wasteful agricultural methods. His wife does most of the work except for plowing. At present he owns about 40 per cent of the Union's cattle, a useless ostentation, which he is discouraged by his social custom from using for food. Overstocking denudes large areas and the Bantu is reluctant to use even manure as a fertilizer. The number of cattle in native areas is substantial, the last official reports showing an aggregate of some 3,700,000 animals. Curiously enough, government control of animal diseases helps to keep the herds alive.

But the guilt of overstocking does not rest on natives

alone. In 1950, during a boom in the price of wool, so many farmers kept such large numbers of sheep that the denuding of the veld was estimated as being more damaging than five years of drought.

A labor-tenant system for European farms arises out of reserve policies. When there is a drought or when the reserve native is unable to provide the barest minimum, he often leaves to hire himself out to a Boer farmer. Formerly he was paid in use of land for personal farming and grazing and could have his family with him. This system has partially disappeared, and he is now often paid in wages. Legislation passed in 1932 provided that every farm servant must give not less than a hundred and eighty days' work to his master each year — but to insure his staying, he must work on days of his employer's choice. Because of this law, service can be spread over a term of an entire year. Between 1933, the year of a widespread famine, and 1936, the natives suffered terribly. In some districts, natives deliberately informed the police that they had not paid their poll tax, hoping to get arrested and sent to jail, where they would get something to eat.

These conditions in themselves prevent intensive effort on the part of the native, even were he capable of it. But the Boers, many of whom are hardly superior to the natives in their farming methods, do not object. The story runs that a Boer in the northern Transvaal, who was complaining bitterly of drought conditions, was asked whether he had dug irrigation ditches. The Boer, apparently astonished, replied, "The Lord knows best. I must not seek to hinder his work. If it doesn't rain, the Lord means it not to. I will dig no ditches." There are still ministers in the Dutch Reformed Church who condemn scientific progress and political and economic reform. Such ministers teach that machines are ungodly and sinful and that the wrath of the Lord will smite those who employ them. It is from European farms, which are generally backward, that the bulk of the Union's food must come.

If the native, forced to leave his reserve, does not wish to work on a farm, he may go to the mines or to the city, where he is likely to be better paid — another incidental cause for friction between British industry and Boer farming. At the mines the natives live in compounds, separated from their families. Industry or domestic service attracts the native to the cities, where he lives in "locations," often badly overcrowded slums. In urban areas, as well as in the reserves, he must pay a local hut tax, a device to encourage mining labor. When large numbers of able-bodied men are kept away from the reserves, there is even less care of the soil.

Whether, in the three-century sequence of men and events, a more and just humane solution for the native populations could have been evolved is not within our present consideration. The fact remains that the nine million natives in the Union of South Africa are considered chiefly as a natural resource to be used for the benefit of a white minority. The reserves are little more than labor reservoirs from which a supply can be taken when necessary and returned when the need diminishes. This is borne out by the attitude of the present government which is legislating constantly stricter control of natives. (Dr. Malan, re-elected in 1953 as prime minister, stated recently that his policy of total segregation is "based on the Christian principles of justice and reasonableness.") The Urban Areas Act is designed to remove "surplus" natives from cities and return them to the reserves. Surplus natives are those not being used. When they are needed, they will be permitted to return. How the already overcrowded, badly eroded reserves will provide for them while they are waiting is not disclosed.

Still, efforts for general improvement are being made. There is a far-reaching government plan in the Soil Conservation Act of 1946. The act, which applies to all land in the Union, provides:

1. An overall *conservation board*.
2. Farmers may form, in conjunction, *conservation districts*, to be helped by the board.
3. The state may intervene directly into any area and form a *conservation area*.
4. The state is given powers of expropriation of farms

or suspension of farming rights where action is considered necessary.

5. Liberal *financial assistance* to farms.

The act is handicapped by some usual problems, a "shortage of qualified and experienced personnel" and the fact that it will take "several years" to build up conservation service to full strength. The 1951 report of the Soil Conservation Board complains of the wide disparity between government rates of pay and those offered by private enterprise.

The final word on achievement should come from the Director of Soil Conservation himself, Mr. J. C. Ross:

> . . . the situation as regards erosion and desiccation over the Union as a whole has not improved, but deteriorated steadily as the years have passed. All the destructive practices that give rise to erosion are still rife in farming today. The record of past achievements by the state is no mean one, but notwithstanding all that has been done for the betterment of farming by way of research and experimentation, education, propaganda, advisory and regulatory services, improved marketing and distribution, price control, reduced tariffs, subsidization of anti-erosion works, drought relief and various other forms of state assistance, there is little evidence of general improvement in the systems of farming over the Union as a whole.

The situation within the native reserves is even worse and here the lack of improvement is obviously not solely due to inadequate personnel nor to the disparity in pay. Other reasons of failure include the facts that among the Africans general education is not compulsory, and that less than half of them have any kind of school opportunity. Even the lunch subsidies, which attracted children to schools, were recently reduced on economic grounds. One incident is particularly illuminating. A number of years ago the Rockefeller Foundation indicated its interest in the building of a medical school for natives. This foundation actually made a firm offer towards such an end. Finally, this offer had to be withdrawn in the face of government policy, which was not prepared to grant such facilities to the native peoples.

It is easy to theorize regarding a situation such as this and to point out that, whatever the presumed justifications, no ultimate solution of the South African problem can be reached through such a policy. One cannot too greatly blame a society for the historical backgrounds that influence its actions. However, we can justly criticize any government which is entirely subservient to traditional values and incapable of adjustment to changing circumstances.

It is not within the purpose of this book to deal with social conditions as such but rather to endeavor to illustrate their powerful influence, together with the impact of growing populations, upon the availability and development of agricultural and other natural resources. The situation in South Africa is in many respects exceptional. Its story, including some of its historical aspects, has been related here in some detail because this country so vividly refutes the statement frequently made that the world problem of adequate food supply can readily be resolved if present technical knowledge regarding agriculture could be generally put into practice. Similar and equally potent barriers of a cultural or social nature exist in innumerable other countries throughout the world. It is a delusion to disregard them. South Africa is an example, even though a somewhat extreme one, of a country where, in the face of existing social and political conditions, all the forces of science and technology can accomplish little.

VII. THE AMAZON

*Is its vastness
designed for man?*

In the ever-increasing discussion as to whether the earth is capable of providing for more and more people, certain great tropical regions, still little used, are frequently spoken of as potential reserves which, if properly developed, could provide large quantities of essential resources as well as living room for excess populations from other lands.

Of all such regions the great Amazon Valley stands out as the most provocative and challenging, not only because of its vastness but also because, so far, very little human use has been made of it. Consequently, it can be selected as an arch example of a retarded region about which both hope and pessimism are voiced in the present great debate regarding peoples and their resources. What sorts of difficulties — what kinds of handicaps — must be overcome to bring a backward area such as this into the design of a more productive earth? Is it true that this one twentieth of the land surface of the globe awaits only the alchemy of know-how, together with more people and more capital, to make it flourish? The impression exists that it should be almost as simple as that. It is very clear, however, that it is about as difficult to change and improve the character of a landscape as the character and social habits of man himself. In considering the Amazon, neither the one nor the other can be overlooked.

Why is this immense region, discovered and explored eighty years before the Pilgrims came to Plymouth, still almost as unproductive as it was four centuries ago? The very size of the Amazon Valley gives us pause. Nearly two fifths of the entire South American continent lies within this basin shared by six sovereign nations. Is it but coincidence that not one of these countries has been able to make more than superficial use of its possession — especially since most of them have regional surplus population problems themselves! There must be reasons. Space on this crowded earth is at a premium; yet as in the Sahara and the boreal forests of Canada, fewer than two persons per square mile have seen fit to make their homes in the Amazon Valley to date.

It would be odd indeed if so much territory were all alike. The Amazon landscape is many things, but most important it is two massive pieces: a wide outer shell of foothills and mountains almost surrounding a flat inner basin. This inner basin is the smaller portion — a million square miles. Yet that is more than the British Isles, France, Sweden, Poland, Germany and Spain all put together. It has a population of about two million people, compared with more than as many hundred millions in those European countries. The outer rim is nearly twice as large. It is this massive barrier — including the highlands of Brazil, Venezuela and the Guianas, and the great range of the Andes to the west — which, more than the deep forests of the inner basin, have made it difficult for man to penetrate the Amazonian country. Here is one of the last retreats of primitive man in all the world. In this formidable band of rough terrain between the navigable streams of the inner basin and the villages of herdsmen, farmers, and miners on the periphery of the mountain shell, hide the last tribes of aboriginal Americans who live as their ancestors lived centuries before the voyage of Columbus. They hold the sanctuary only because, as yet, the white man has not wanted it. Already the most primitive Indians have retreated from the inner basin, where every navigable stream has been explored.

Only Peru has constructed an overland highway across the mountain wall to connect its economic heartland with a navigable stream of the inner basin. This engineering achievement — extending five hundred miles from Lima across the Andes to Pucallpa on the Ucayali River — was completed in 1943. Yet so costly is motor transport that much cargo still travels six thousand miles by ship from Callao, Lima's port on the Pacific coast, via the Panama Canal, the western Atlantic and finally up the Amazon to eastern Peru. Brazil is in the process of building its first overland route from Rio to navigable Amazonian waters. The air-line distance of this road to Pôrto Velho on the Madeira River is some sixteen hundred miles — equivalent to that between New York and Denver. It remains to be discovered how many actual miles it will be forced to wind through the broken terrain. Yet when it is completed no merchant will dream of sending wheat in or rubber out by motor truck because the cheaper way will still be by river and the sea. The mountain shell will be the last of Amazonia to challenge occupation and development. The inner basin, laced with some fifty thousand miles of navigable streams — twice the circumference of the globe — will receive the most attention long before. This inner basin, a million square miles, represents a fiftieth of the world's land.

Of all ways to move cargo, water is the cheapest. No other part of the world so large as the inner Amazon Basin has such a magnificent system of interconnecting waterways designed without the least assistance by the hand of man. Some scientists who have examined this amazing network of streams flowing from three sides of a continent into one single, tremendous artery say the largest portion of the land over which it flows was once the bottom of an inland sea. That was millions of years ago, before the Andes were born — when rocks, since lifted upward by titanic thrusts and scoured by pressures of ice and snow three miles high above the level of the Pacific, were once washed by tides of that same ocean. Then came a time of cataclysmic change, when the Andes were slowly pushed upward out of the sea and the land by massive movements of the earth's crust. As the mountains emerged, they shut off the Pacific outlet of what we now call the Amazon, damming it up into a great inland sea that eventually spilled over to the east, cutting its present outlet through to the Atlantic.

During the eon of time this inland sea was in existence, billions of tons of sand, silt and clay were eroded from the surrounding mountain shores and flushed into the vast body of water, where they settled on the bottom, smoothly carpeting its rocky surface. To this day the subsequent carving of stream channels through these soft and comparatively level sediments has exposed only a few scattered traces of the buried rocks. Thus the navigable rivers of our time are unimpeded by bedrock outcrops which would tear the hulls of ships.

The sea-bottom genesis of the inner Amazon region resulted in an amazingly flat land surface after the water drained away. A man standing atop the Empire State Building in New York, 1250 feet in height, is four times higher above sea level than he would be on the banks of the Amazon at Iquitos, Peru, 2300 miles upstream from the river's mouth. This extreme flatness is almost beyond belief. Were it not for the tremendous volumes of water pouring from its myriad tributaries, all fed by torrential equatorial rains, commercial shipping up to the foothills of the Andes would be impossible. This unique low-altitude characteristic of such a great continental interior is the Amazon's greatest physical advantage from the standpoint of economic penetration. Here motor launches are able to navigate in seasons of high rainfall to points as far as 3600 miles from the Atlantic entrance to the great river system without encountering either falls or obstructing rapids. This is a distance almost as far as that from Juneau, Alaska to Guatemala City, Guatemala — all without the benefit of a single man-made alteration of the channel either by locks, levees or dredgings. Eleven tributaries of the main stream are navigable for over a thousand miles from their confluence with the main artery, which itself is navigable from the Atlantic to within two hundred miles of the Pacific.

During the season of low water, when the rains slacken between June and October, the levels of the principal river channels may fall more than forty feet at some points, exposing sand bars and leaving only narrow tortuous avenues that will not safely accommodate large ships. The navigable extent of the Purús River, one of the longest tributaries, shrinks from a maximum of 2000 miles in the rainy season to 1650 miles in the dry season. The speed of the current in the main stream may drop from six to two miles an hour.

At Manaus, which is 1040 miles from the Atlantic yet only 125 feet above sea level, the Rio Negro has fluctuated between a maximum depth of 94 feet at high water and a minimum of 45 feet at low. At Iquitos, Peru, 350 feet above sea level and 2300 miles from the Atlantic, the Amazon may rise to a depth of nearly 90 feet at high water and drop below 50 feet during the comparatively dry months. Differences as great as 55 feet between high and low water have been recorded on the upper Juruá.

So flat is the inner basin that the effect of ocean tides has been noted at Obidos, 665 miles from the mouth of the Amazon — a distance equivalent to that between Chicago and Oklahoma City or between London and Venice. Though the tides back up the waters of the river, they do so only by raising its level at the mouth, for the current of the river is so powerful that salt water cannot push its way against it. The rush of silt-laden waters into the Atlantic discolors the ocean two hundred miles beyond the point where the river enters the sea. So enormous is the volume of water flowing in the Amazon system that it has been estimated that one fifth of all the river waters of the earth belong to it. At its mouth the stream divides into two channels to engulf the world's largest fluvial island — Marajó — which alone exceeds the area of Switzerland.

When the floods during the rainy season overflow the river's banks, the waters create vast inland lakes studded with islands. Thousands of new sloughs and lagoons are born and the river itself may develop as many as three or four principal channels. The whole riverine body thus created will at times reach a breadth of twenty to thirty miles, all moving across hundreds of thousands of square miles toward the ocean. So impressive is this fluvial world that the Amazon is known as "O Rio Mar" — the River Sea.

Of such enormity is the silt load sucked from the banks by the swirling currents that the five billion tons of sediments annually discharged into the Atlantic would spread a blanket of alluvium half a foot deep over the entire state of Massachusetts. What a boon to the Amazon farmers if this could be salvaged and used! But it is lost forever as it sweeps out to the ocean, scarcely forming any appreciable delta. The continental shelf at the mouth of the river has subsided to so low a level, and both the river and ocean currents are so strong, that the silt is carried far beyond the immediate shore before it is deposited. Unlike the Nile, the Mississippi, the Ganges or the Irrawaddy, there is no great area of rich agricultural land provided at its mouth by this giant river, which of all others might have built up the most extensive alluvial plains had the contours of the marine shelf been appropriate and the drag of the Atlantic's south equatorial current not so powerful. Experimental efforts to trap a portion of these fluvial silts to fill in the great swamps of the middle and lower river margins have been initiated in recent years by the Brazilian government and appear to be meeting with success.

The climate is not so easily appraised, for it is both help and hindrance. There was a time, before more than a few persons of the temperate zones became acquainted with equatorial life, when an impressive mythology was created by adventurers and sojourners, who related fantastic accounts of oppressive heat and perpetual deluge. But since World War II, when hundreds of thousands in the armed services found they could not only live but could wage campaigns as well in the humid tropics, a version closer to the truth has begun to emerge. Is the equatorial region such an uninhabitable part of the earth?

If one takes a map and draws his finger across the earth's equatorial belt, taking in an area 10° north and south of the line, he will include most of the basins of the Amazon and the Congo. These, to be sure, are sparsely populated regions. Then as he proceeds across the Indian Ocean he will find his swath includes the island of Ceylon and the southern tip of India, where human numbers per square mile are among the highest in the world. Then he comes to Indonesia's island of Java, another area of extreme population density. Can it be that climatic stress accounts for the sparsity of man in the Amazon Basin, whereas he is so numerous in some other equatorial areas?

Temperature data recorded at Belém indicate that the extreme maximum for that city at the mouth of the Amazon is 95° Fahrenheit. At Manaus the highest temperature ever registered was 101°, although the average annual maximum is but 89°. If one is searching for record high temperatures outside the zones of deserts, he may be surprised to find that Toronto, Canada, has experienced a maximum of 103°; Calcutta, India, 110°; and Fort Yukon, Alaska, 100°. The Amazon Valley is not the place to look for the highest temperatures, not even the highest mean temperatures in the humid regions of the earth. Many a city in the United States or Europe has broiled under more intense heat than has ever been experienced in an Amazonian village. A New Yorker might find a slight relief from the hot spells of July and August by escaping to Belém. The notable characteristic of the warm climate of the Amazon region is its monotony.

Annual rainfall, while heavy, is not, as is commonly thought, extraordinarily high in the Amazon Valley. Some sections, particularly near the upper reaches of navigability in Peru and Bolivia, may receive as much as 125 inches each year. Belém's average is 93 inches and that for Manaus 72. Such precipitation is considerable when compared with 57 for New Orleans, 33 for Chicago, and 43 for New York. But it is not extreme when compared with 150 inches at Ketchikan, Alaska; 81 for Bergen, Norway; 95 for Singapore; or 460 for Waialeale, Hawaii, which is indeed exceptional.

For all its rainfall, scarcely a day passes in the Amazonian lowlands when the sun does not appear, and wide expanses of blue vault the sky at least for short intervals. Often the early hours of the morning are devoid of any overcast and not until noon or after do banks of clouds begin to drift in over the forests. Rain itself usually commences late in the afternoon or evening after the day's work has been finished, and ceases long before morning. The citizen of the British Isles, accustomed to the monotonous gray skies of his fog-banked homeland, as well as the voyager from the United States, who at home has experienced week-long periods of heavy rains and intermittent showers, often notes with surprised delight the quick passing of the equatorial showers and the almost invariable clear blue of the morning sky on the Amazon. In the central portion of the valley, droughts are sometimes experienced between June and October.

The climate does have its economic consequences. The absence of frost means that vegetation remains green and succulent most of the year. Even during the periods of moderate rainfall, between May and October, there is usually sufficient moisture to produce such seasonal crops as rice, beans, and corn, while the perennials such as bananas, mangoes, sugar cane and citrus fruits are unimpaired except in the central portion of the valley, where droughts of one to three months' duration may occur. Pasture grasses being available the year around make the tending and foraging of cattle an easy matter. House gardens can be depended upon for some supplementary food supplies for the family kitchen each month. A principal drawback of a year without frost or intense desiccation is the difficulty of suppressing or eradicating numerous parasites of economic plants, domestic animals and man. Once established, a serious parasitic fungus may ravage a whole plantation, as the South American leaf disease almost entirely destroyed the Ford Company's rubber groves at Fordlandia on the Tapajóz River. Except in a few communities where special control measures are taken, the ubiquitous anopheles mosquito breeds unsuppressed as a carrier of malarial scourge. Leaf-cutting *sauba* ants do extensive damage. Local settlers often build gardens on raised platforms to assure a crop. There is an old saying: "Destroy the sauba or the sauba will destroy Brazil." But conditions of these sorts are not peculiarly Amazonian. In most parts of the humid tropics, man, animal and plant must contend with the same or equally serious afflictions. Climate, however, is not the sole culprit. For instance, people in few communities in the world enjoy such a high standard of living as United States citizens in the Panama Canal Zone; yet climatic conditions there are not very dissimilar to those of the Amazon area. In the Canal Zone, however, diet, sanitation and economic opportunity are incomparably superior. North Americans employed there work about as hard physically and mentally as people in the United States, and vital statistics fail to indicate that climate adversely affects them.

Getting enough food for local consumption has been a problem in the Amazon Valley from the beginning of European settlement to the present day. Some four hundred years ago, when Francisco de Orellana led his little band of fifty-eight Spanish adventurers on the first exploration from the Andes to the Atlantic, they aroused Indian hostility all along the way by their desperate demands for food. In reporting his ascent of the river to Iquitos in the U.S.S. *Wilmington* in 1899, Commander Todd related that: "The crying need of the Amazon Valley is food for the people. . . . At the small towns along the river it is nearly impossible to obtain beef, vegetables, or fruit of any sort, and its inhabitants depend largely upon river fish, mandioc, and canned food for their subsistence." As though he were rephrasing a theme recorded over and over again by most travelers in that labyrinthian river world, Dr. Felisberto C. de Camargo, Director of Agricultural Research in the Brazilian Amazon, informed the United

Nations in 1948 that the people of the region were as yet unable to feed themselves, let alone provide surpluses for a hungry world. "Belém, capital of the state of Pará, is today importing meat by airplane from northern Goiás . . . On each flight the two-motored plane transports five tons of boned meat which sells in Belém for 10 cruzeiros a kilogram." At that time ten cruzeiros, about 50 cents, was the average daily wage in the Belém. The kilogram is two and two tenths pounds.

Beans, one of the most important staples of the local diet, must each year be shipped into the valley from southern Brazil despite the fact that beans can be grown locally. In 1946, 56 per cent of the Brazilian Amazon's bean supply and nearly all its lard, butter, cheese and processed milks were thus purchased. To those who had looked upon that area as a refuge for the hungry and displaced peoples of Europe, Dr. Camargo cautioned: "The Amazon can offer no solution without in the first place solving the production of food supplies essential for the life of man."

Most of the inner basin lies inside Brazilian territory, but a fairly sizable portion belongs to Peru, and lesser amounts to Colombia, Bolivia, Venezuela and Ecuador. Over a million and a half Brazilians make up about four fifths of the total population of the inner basin. Of these Brazilians, roughly a million live by gathering forest products and by a type of agriculture which might more aptly be described as subsistence gardening. The others live in towns and in the two main cities of Belém and Manaus. The Peruvian population is divided in about the same proportions. The people of the other nationalities are almost entirely rural.

The population of the inner basin is by no means evenly distributed, even outside the main cities. The greatest densities occur near the mouth of the river on its southern bank and on the island of Marajó. Between Belém and Bragança, near the Atlantic coast, runs a railroad a hundred and eighty miles long. It was built partly for the purpose of encouraging agricultural development along its right of way in the hope that rural settlers would produce a surplus food supply for the city of Belém. Comparatively dense populations have grown up along the route of the railway, but subsistence gardening rather than commercial agriculture characterizes the husbandry of the people. Little surplus food is sent to Belém. Along the nine hundred miles of riverbank between Belém and Manaus there are scores of villages and a few towns, including Santarém, Óbidos, Parintins, and Itacoatiara. Human occupation, rural and urban, has clung to the stream banks. It was there the Indians lived before the immigrant rubber tapper arrived and it is there that white settlements have been most successful. The explanation is simple. People must move about to find wild game and forest products. To get around and to communi-

cate with one another they find the canoe more con-
venient than an overland trail. The vast expanses of
the jungle which lie far inland from the rivers are
practically uninhabited. The people might most ap-
propriately be described as "bank dwellers." If one
were to sketch a map of the Amazon region's population distribution, it would resemble the pattern of an
oak leaf's veining. At the base of the leaf — the river's
mouth and widest portion of the midrib — the heaviest
concentration would be noted. Then there would be a
gradual diminution toward the margins of the leaf as
the main rib forked and reforked. Only a few sections
of the population map would differ from the progres-
sively finer lines of the oak-leaf veins. At Manaus and
Iquitos there would be conspicuous concentrations. The
Acre Territory at the head of navigation on the Purús
and Jurúa would be more densely populated as would
the Upper Madeira in Brazil and its affluent, the Beni
in Bolivia. These latter regions were heavy producers
of rubber during the boom days early in this century
and have remained more densely settled than most sections of the basin.

Although access to the river has influenced the pattern of settlement most of all, it is a fortunate coincidence that the best soils are those of the flood plain.
The soils on lands high above the annual inundations
are densely cloaked with luxuriant forest vegetation,
but attempts to clear and plant these upland soils to

clean, tilled crops almost invariably end in disappointment. Thousands of years of equatorial rains and warmth have weathered these soils to the point where they are almost exhausted of mineral nutrient reserves. Only the humus, constantly restored by the shedding of tons of leaves over each acre of ground, keeps the soil alive and fertile. So long as the trees remain undisturbed and generation after generation of forest succeeds each other, an endless cycle of humus creation and exhaustion goes on. As the humus decays, nutrient elements are released to the living roots and these in turn provide the elements to the leaves which again eventually become humus. But break this cycle once — remove the forest canopy and let the millions of microorganisms which live by destruction of the humus have their last good feast — and all the nutrient by-products of their activity are flushed out of the soil by the following rains, because the tree roots are not there to soak up the soil solution and recapture the vital elements. This deterioration does not happen overnight, as nature does not operate so suddenly. But within two or three years the subsistence farmer usually finds his yields declining and he abandons old clearings for new.

The amount of labor spent in the continuous process of clearing and abandoning the soils above the flood plain is so excessive that foods raised there are generally so costly the Amazonian farmer is not often attracted to commercial agriculture, for there are other places in the tropics where soil conditions are better and costs of production less. Farmers from these other areas — for instance, productive lands in Cuba, Guatemala, Trinidad, Jamaica or Honduras — can outstrip the Amazonian in market competition. The upland soils are frequently of good physical structure and respond to commercial fertilizers, but the cost of these commercial fertilizers is generally prohibitive in the Amazon Valley; consequently, they are almost never used. Agronomists seem to agree that, at a cost, such soils could be made productive. Actually, it is possible to make even sterile beach sands yield crops if cost is disregarded. But in the framework of a world economy, costs of production in agriculture, as in other activities, cannot be disregarded in realistic appraisals of the potentialities of the Amazon area. Approximately 97 per cent of the soils of the inner basin are above the flood plain! Wisest of all uses for this land would be commercial tree crops. The world is experiencing a shortage of vegetable oils; yet there are among the tropical palms a number of excellent oil producers. The African oil palm, actually a Brazilian native, in particular has done well commercially under climate and soil conditions similar to those of the Amazonian uplands, although yields are reduced when droughts occur.

The great river basin is the homeland of the rubber tree, cacao, tonka bean, tagua, Brazil nut, rosewood and mahogany. Developments in the Belgian Congo have demonstrated that tropical forests can be successfully converted to tree-crop plantations without seriously upsetting the biological and nutrient complex of the soils. In the Amazon Basin there are as yet important economic and social hurdles to this type of development. We will consider them in a moment when we look at the land tenure and mercantile systems, which in the last analysis are probably the region's severest handicaps.

What of the river flood plain where the better soils are found? These were mapped in 1952 by two tireless men, C. F. Marbut and C. B. Manifold, and their studies show that only approximately 3 or 4 per cent of the entire inner basin is subject to annual inundation. Somewhat more than half the island of Marajó is covered, and there are sections along the main channel between Manaus and Gurupá where the banks overflow for distances of twenty to thirty miles — sizable areas, to be sure, but small in comparison with the total. No adequate land-use survey has ever been made of the region which would permit a precise statement of the extent of usable alluvial soils on this great flood plain. During the season of light rains, crops such as corn, rice, beans, and watermelons can be raised successfully after the water levels recede. The crops mature and are harvested before the floods return. At a guess — exact figures being unavailable — there are possibly as many as ten thousand square miles thus made temporarily available every year. This is land upon which fertility is restored with each succeeding flood by depositions of relatively unweathered silts and clays gouged out of upstream banks by the rushing currents of rivers with their rise of thirty to fifty feet when in full swell. The major economic disadvantage of the alluvial lands is the uneven, patchy pattern of their distribution. There is little handicap to subsistence farmers working with hand tools. People with limited resources, laboring in such a manner, cannot till more than a few acres per family. The possibility of large-scale operations, however, without heavy capital investments in dykes, drainage systems and pumps for the cultivation of paddy rice are much more limited. It is from such land, however, that much of the valley's food staples and its jute fiber are obtained.

Of the vast area lying within the forested expanse of the Brazilian inner basin, only an infinitesimal five hundred square miles are cultivated — less than half the area of little Rhode Island! This represents about one fifth of an acre of land per inhabitant, or slightly over one third of an acre for every rural resident. The total value of all agricultural production in this region did not amount to ten million dollars in 1946. Forest products — chiefly rubber, nuts, rosewood oil, chicle and mahogany — were worth about thirty million dollars. The whole value of agricultural and forest extractive occupations yielded less than the plum and prune crops of the United States in the same year! Since over one million persons were engaged in forest exploitation and agriculture, the total value of their efforts for the whole year of 1946 was about forty dollars per capita. Cattle on the savannas of Goiás earned as much per head munching grass as did humans by field and forest labor in the lowlands of the Brazilian Amazon.

Such profits as are made in the valley are derived from commercial activities. The level of living of the people producing the articles of trade is about as low as is humanly tolerable, a fact generally overlooked by those who would encourage the immigration of displaced persons because food supply and economic opportunities are inadequate in Europe! To be sure, only a small part of the potential agricultural land is now being used, and the forests might be considered limitless, but these do not afford even the present populations a respectable existence.

There is little doubt that all crops raised elsewhere in the world's humid lowland tropics can be produced in the Amazon Basin. If the question uppermost in the world's mind is whether the valley will accommodate millions more subsistence farmers and forest gleaners, the answer is doubtless affirmative. If, on the other hand, it is anticipated that the Amazon Valley can become a greater producer of surpluses deliverable to the congested regions of the globe to relieve their hunger, there are as yet no reasonable grounds to support such hopes. The conditions under which crops might be grown there commercially are such as to put costs of production substantially above world trade levels. The valley might eventually accommodate forty to fifty million persons at the bare subsistence stage now prevailing. One can well deliberate whether such an eventuality would prove more of a calamity than an achievement. Perhaps, if the earth's population pressures become so intense that all staple foods are to sell at prices created by urgent demand — when even more of our incomes are spent simply to feed ourselves — then these now marginal areas within the inner Amazon Basin may have their day. One wonders after that — what?

While we may be captivated by the possibility of the Amazon's accommodating the surplus populations of congested countries or providing extra food to feed them, the sobering realization of the perennial inability of the people already there to feed themselves well thrusts itself upon us. True, the total area of land under cultivation is increasing — but so are human numbers, at one of the fastest rates anywhere. During the half century between 1890 and 1940 the population of the whole inner basin tripled. During that same interval the people of Java, Puerto Rico and Japan slightly more than doubled their numbers. The United States population almost doubled during those years. Neither

Italy nor India increased so rapidly. Latin America as a whole is experiencing an amazing multiplication rate. Do these trends suggest that, given time, the inhabitants of Amazonia will multiply until their homeland too will be one of the densely settled portions of the earth? It is by no means an impossibility.

In the *municipio* of Belém, beyond the limits of the city itself, rural residents had reached a density of forty persons per square mile by 1940. The city of Belém had grown from 18,000 to 230,000 in the century between 1851 and 1950. Manaus, the capital of Amazonas, had emerged from a village of 4188 in 1839 into a metropolis of 110,000 by 1950. Iquitos, in Peru, did not exist ninety years ago; yet in 1948 it had 40,000 citizens. Other instances of population growth could be cited, although care must be taken not to place too much reliance on the adequacy of the population data for the Amazon territory in the early censuses.

Today the people of the Amazon are chiefly native-born. However, tracing their ancestry back several generations, one finds them to be predominantly of Portuguese, Spanish, Syrian, Negro and local Indian stock. The foreign-born, including those who have become naturalized since immigrating, constitute less than 2 per cent of the valley's populations. These aliens are, however, from almost all the states of Europe as well as from many parts of Asia, Africa and North America. The world's commerce in tropical products of the

Amazon has brought traders, sailors and adventurers from all corners of the earth into the valley, where some have remained to try their fortunes. From time to time organized colonization has been attempted. Confederate refugees from the United States founded several settlements after the Civil War. Most abandoned the projects but a few remained. Negroes, few in number, were brought in during the years of slavery. In the twentieth century the Japanese established successful settlements in the lower Amazon, where they engaged in the production of jute and rice. But the most important influx of peoples into the great river valley has been from the drought-ridden states of northeastern Brazil: Ceará and Piauí. Ever since the rubber boom, these people have found employment in the valley when driven by crop failures and hunger to abandon their home territories. Evidently the climate of the Amazon has not dissuaded some persons from diverse regions of the earth from settling in the valley.

Perhaps it is because there were so few people in this region a hundred years ago that the number of their descendants is not relatively large today. The original seed supply being small, the harvest has not been impressive. But if one were to project the future population on the basis of its increase during the past fifty years, it seems possible that it might reach seven or eight millions by the year 2000 and conceivably twenty million a hundred years hence. The concern of some of the most intelligent Amazonians is not that their valley will remain underpopulated but that it might one day swarm with poor rice and manioc growers whose existence would be on a par with that of the present-day subsistence farmers and forest gleaners. At the present time the Amazon may well be said not to lack people so much as it lacks opportunity for those who are already there.

Have we as civilized people really focused our attention upon the most vital aspect of this complex question of living space, congestion, food surpluses and deficits? Are we not running such a busy race after food, space and employment for ever greater numbers that we are forgetting the purpose of it all — a better living for human beings? What is humanitarianism? Is it trying to disperse and feed more people or is its objective a better quality of living for each individual and for mankind as a whole? Do we really wish to see how much pressure the earth and the human spirit can sustain, or are we concerned with fostering the well-being of each infant, whose life is the responsibility of the collective "us"? Conjuring with such thoughts, let's, for a moment, turn our attention more closely to why those who are now here aren't fed very well.

Rivers and streams being the highways and byways of the region, lands beyond easy access to navigable water are of little or no commercial value. By custom the man who owns the riverbank is acknowledged sovereign of the forests and occasional grasslands lying in the interior beyond the bounds of his property. The best soils, since they lie within the flood plain of the river, mantle lands near navigable water and are included within the bounds of stream-bank properties. Ownership of the stream bank thus is ownership of the only important economic assets in the rural areas of the basin.

These facts accent the circumstance that nearly all riparian lands throughout the inner basin are already in individual or corporate hands, either in fee simple or by government lease. When one considers the vast space of the valley, together with its sparse populations, it would seem without further examination that there is boundless terrain available for homestead settlement. But this is not the case, although the governments could, by changing their land lease policies, make it so. Even on the remote Casiquiare River — that little stream in Venezuela linking the waters of the Orinoco to those of the Rio Negro of the Amazon system — even on this river of little consequence every mile of stream bank is mapped, plotted and assigned to an owner or lessee. It is the same with all the thousands of miles of riparian lands, whether they are under the sovereignty of Brazil, Peru, Venezuela, Bolivia, Ecuador or Colombia. Not only is the fluvial basin definitely not terra incognita but its useful parts are already owned or assigned.

Brazil holds political control over most of the Amazon, and fortunately Brazilian census data make possible a rather accurate evaluation of the land-tenure picture in the states of Amazonas, and in Pará and the Territory of Acre. Within these political subdivisions there were nearly one and a half million people in 1940. Seventy-one per cent of these inhabitants lived beyond the bounds of towns and villages, dependent upon forest-gathering agriculture for existence. In this whole region there were 81,000 properties. No statistics indicate exactly how many persons lived on their own land, but assuming five individuals per family, presumably 40 per cent of the rural people belonged to families which had at least a little land of their own. What is startling is that about 60 per cent did not.

In other words, in this region, one of the most sparsely populated in the world, 60 per cent of the rural people are already obliged to live and work on the estates of others because they have no land of their own. This is a fact deserving reflection by designers of resettlement schemes who dream of shifting land-hungry peasants from one continent to another — even the peon of the Amazon might apply.

But this is not the whole story of land tenure in the Brazilian territory. Of the 1.3 million square miles in Amazonas, Pará and Acre only 100,000 are in the hands of proprietors. But these 100,000 square miles are the all important riparian lands. The balance lies in the relatively useless beyond. Neither do ships reach them nor might settlers penetrate without violating the rights of the shore proprietors. Of the strategically located riparian properties, 81 per cent are in large estates of over 2500 acres and owned by a scant 4 per cent of the proprietors. Another 10 per cent of the lands are held by 7.5 per cent of the proprietors. In other words, about 91 per cent of the area suitable for agriculture and forest gathering is controlled by fewer than 10,000 owners.

Is it possible that the land tenure system is to an important extent responsible for the retarded economic development of the valley? This concentration of lands in the hands of a relatively few owners is not particularly Amazonian in character but rather generally true throughout Latin America. It is as old as the Iberian conquest and the feudal system of land management set up by the Portuguese and Spanish. Some students believe it is a major factor in the retarded technological and economic condition of our neighbors to the south.

Apparently the land-tenure system is to an important extent responsible for the slow development of the valley. It discourages immigration and settlement by persons who might be willing to pioneer on free land but who are without funds to purchase properties. Those who own estates are usually incapable of developing more than a fraction of their capacity, through lack of man power and capital. To encourage settlement upon estate lands, the owners, known as "donos" (patrons), offer garden plots and cash advances to prospective tenants. Debts are paid in produce from the garden or the forests. Once indebted to a dono, a peon is not permitted to leave the property until his account is paid. Frequently he never quite catches up with his account. He becomes a desultory workman at best, resigned to an improvident existence.

The land-holding system is, however, only one of the major factors contributing to the retarded economic situation. Statistics reveal what is also apparent to the eye, namely, that thousands of independent families possess their own small plots of ground upon which are produced subsistence crops as well as market surpluses — the latter usually forest products. In Brazilian Pará, Amazonas and Acre, there are about sixty thousand small holdings ranging from less than 2.5 acres to as much as 125 acres. Perhaps as many as three hundred thousand people, or almost 30 per cent of the rural population, live on these modest homesteads, mostly concentrated near the mouth of the main river and along its principal channels and associated sloughs between Belém and Manaus. Possibly most of the 60 per cent of the rural people who are without lands of their own would like to be proprietors of such holdings rather than peons on large estates. They could more easily achieve such an ambition if it were not for the difficulty of acquiring credit. And it must be said in fairness that it would be risky and unprofitable for individuals to lend money for such a purpose.

It takes keen and experienced individuals to invest money profitably in a retarded region. Because of hazards involved, credit necessarily is hard to come by, hedged with restrictive conditions, and weighted with high interest rates. Even most patrons or donos are men of extremely modest means, who would be unable to finance their own operations requiring advances to peons if they were not in turn given credit by merchants who deal in commodities the basin furnishes the outside world, and in supplies of hand tools, textiles, simple clothing, food and medicines brought in from the outside. The merchants in turn are usually dependent for their financial strength upon credit relationships with major export-import establishments in the cities of Belém, Manaus and Iquitos. Money is so difficult for the indigent to borrow — and too precious for the merchant to lend except on the safest terms — that most men without property cannot graduate from peon status. To acquire property would not only require some capital but, even more important, a reserve would be necessary to support the new homesteader and his family until he could become productive. The commercial-credit economy of the basin can scarcely be expected to take such a risk when the safer way of doing business is by the present system. This is a hard fact which no wishful thinking can ignore.

The geography and practice of public administration in the inner basin is another major handicap to social and economic progress. The sheer difficulty of physical access to the Amazonian provinces of the six countries possessing them make these territories commercially and administratively more remote from the hubs of their particular national societies than if they were separate islands far distant in the sea, beyond homeland coasts. The economic activity of each parent country is oriented along its ocean shores, with the exception of landlocked Bolivia, which nevertheless trades via the Pacific. Their backs are turned away from their almost unapproachable Amazonian interiors.

While mountains separate the valley provinces from parent countries, national political frontiers within the basin separate each from the others. Where the contours of landscape present no obstacle to regional intercourse, men have imposed political barriers! The history of international trade within the basin is laden with incidents of dispute, customs frustrations and a few wars. Curiously, while negligent toward their Amazonian territories in matters of internal policy, the parent countries have not been hesitant to battle one another to extend the frontiers of those economic wastelands. No other portion of the globe comparable in size and landscape unity is so politically subdivided among six sovereign states. And this despite the fact that the people of the basin economically and culturally have more in common than with their respective national societies beyond the mountains.

Most of the valley's capital is furnished by outsiders, either nationals from the capital cities or by foreigners. Consequently, much of the profits of Amazonian trade are siphoned off and not reinvested in permanent improvements. Year after year all the river districts export goods of greater value than they import. This would be an asset of the greatest importance if the wealth thus earned were invested locally. The fact that it is not points to one of the most telling reasons for retarded development. No sovereign state so financially drained could long survive. Here we have a nice example of the weak giving alms to improve the well-being of the stronger.

Centralization of government functions is characteristic of all the countries sharing the Amazon. In effect, most important administrative policy is determined not locally but in remote capital cities where there is little knowledge of or interest in the valley's problems. Rio, Bogotá, Lima, La Paz, Quito and Caracas draw taxes from the people in the interior but return but a small portion to them in the form of public services to aid commerce, agriculture, public health or education. Take a situation in Brazil as a specific example, where the ill effects of existing administrative and tax systems is well illustrated in the case of the city of Belém, with a population, as we have seen, of about 230,000. This city, lying at the mouth of the great river, is the principal municipality of the states of Pará and Amazonas, and indeed of the whole Amazon Basin. Of the taxes currently paid by the residents of these states, approximately 40 per cent goes entirely out of the region and is sent to Rio, the remainder being allocated between the states and municipality, the latter receiving less than one fifth of the total taxes collected. The effects on public health and education are to be anticipated. The average life expectancy of a resident in Belém during the last decade was approximately thirty-six years, as compared with almost twice that in the United States. Similar conditions exist throughout the Brazilian Amazon. Of a total of forty-four towns and cities with populations exceeding a thousand, only eleven were reported in 1940 as having some form of public water supply and only five with sanitary sewers to service at least some of their districts. Due to the dearth of educational facilities resulting from such a system, it is also not surprising that more than half of the people in the Brazilian Amazon can neither read nor write.

One can understand why the man in the interior regions — the man of the Tapajóz, the Beni or the Marañón — shares little of mutual interest with those public officials in remote centers of government who debate and shape policies governing his social and economic life. That he customarily expresses stronger regional pride than national patriotism is scarcely remarkable, feeling as he does so deeply a provincial status he is powerless to modify. To nature's own barriers against progress and national unity, man has contributed his own administrative obstacles.

Amazonia offers no ready welcome. Man, the changer, upon whose efforts economic growth depends, is aided or thwarted by the soundness or weakness of his own self-created ways of life as he is by the richness or poverty of his natural environment. Radical changes for the better of existing political and social conditions in the Amazon Valley, including the removal of the climate of feudalism and a primitive mercantile economy, is the first arduous step. Gradually thereafter man may gain the knowledge, which he does not now possess, of how to cope with the conditions of soil and vegetation which the natural climate of this region creates. At best it will prove a prolonged adventure.

VIII. BEYOND EUROPE
AND EAST OF SUEZ

Burdens of today
—a hope for tomorrow

T HE CONDITIONS in the Western world — in Europe and in the Americas — together with those in Australasia and in Africa represent but part of a situation that faces the human race as a whole. The sequence of considerations in these pages so far is not the result of a desire to seek or magnify the interests of any one nation or even one group of nations or peoples. The present century — the first to do so clearly — demonstrates that the interests of all peoples are interwoven. Actually, we are witnessing a metamorphosis that affects not merely the Western world, or the so-called "free world." All of humanity is involved.

It is natural, no doubt, for one living in the Western world to think and write principally of it or of the regions with which it has closer contact. But there are other reasons. First, due to the cleavage that separates the peoples of the "free world" from those within the iron curtain of the Soviets, there is no present possibility of combined action on a world scale. Consequently, such values as there may be in discussions such as those pursued here would be of greatest use to peoples or governments that are capable of taking co-operative and enlightened action regarding the problems involved. Another reason is that one of the principal efforts in the preceding chapters has been to gain perspective concerning countries that have only recently been "settled" — in the time scale of human history, that is — and also to explore regions of the earth that have barely, as yet, been entered by modern civilization. Consequently, only a few brief comments will be made regarding the countries beyond Europe and east of Suez, although our Western world has an immense amount to take to heart regarding conditions that exist there. Kipling was wrong when he wrote of the East and West that "never the twain shall meet." One of the most brilliant episodes in history is the present stumbling yet determined effort to discover paths of true mutuality and helpfulness between some of the Western nations and some of those on the opposite side of the earth. Eventually, though even long from now, the barriers are bound to dissolve.

Nowhere is the problem of pressures of people more acute than in the Far East. Here there are few open spaces or new horizons. In southern and western Asia there live probably the oldest and certainly the most concentrated clusters of humanity on earth. To the north, reaching from Europe to the far distant shores of the Pacific, lies the giant land of the Soviets. In these regions there exist — or struggle to survive — considerably more than half of all the world's people. In fact, in three lands alone — in Russia, China and the Indian subcontinent — there are more than a billion people.

It is a curious yet suggestive coincidence that the two nations which are dominant in the present fearful struggle between the West and the East have one common physical characteristic. This is that the United States and Russia possess, in relation to their respective populations, almost identically the same amount of land suitable for agriculture. (The population of Russia is about a third again as large as that of the United States and, although current statistics are lacking, is believed to be increasing somewhat more rapidly.) In the United States there are presently some 460,000,000 acres in use, which, divided by the present population, represents about three acres for the subsistence of each individual. In Russia an area of approximately one million square miles of land lends itself to agriculture, lying within a triangle that has its western base extending from Leningrad in the north to the Black Sea in the south and its eastern apex near Lake Baikal. The Ukraine lies within this area. This total of agricultural land is equal to approximately 640,000,000 acres or, in turn, the equivalent of about three acres for each Russian. The United States is more favored, however, as the country extends deep into lower latitudes and, further, can rely more directly upon its surrounding oceans for its rainfall. It will be recalled that rain is derived principally from water drawn, through evaporation, from the oceans and carried landward by the winds and then precipitated. As a consequence, Russia is more susceptible to drought because water drawn into the atmosphere from the Atlantic Ocean and carried eastward by the winds is the source of most of the rainfall throughout Russia. Even in central Siberia more than three quarters of the rain appears to be of Atlantic origin.

As is well known, the Soviets are placing much emphasis on the development of agriculture. How successful the collective farm system will eventually prove is pure conjecture. In this connection the fact that Yugoslavia has only recently abandoned the collectivization of land is highly significant. A recent dispatch from that country stated that the Communist leaders had conceded defeat and have decided to set up the Western type of co-operative as the basic organizational instrument for agricultural production. It is reported that this decision came in the wake of a series of concessions that the Marxist theoreticians were forced to make to the realities of peasant resistance to the collective farm system.*

The situation in the inhabited regions in Asia, and especially in China and in India, is so evident in the sense of population pressures that these countries — containing almost two fifths of all of the people of the world — have come to represent the extremities of suffering that result from too many people on too little land. As China is at present cut off from the Western world, it is impossible to judge the trend of recent events in that country, although there is no reason to believe that its immense population, estimated at more than 450,-000,000 people, is finding relief from the conditions under which it has suffered for so long.

There is ample reason for the widespread attention now being given to India's crisis. It would be an error, however, to think that she, of the Far Eastern countries, has a monopoly on the troubles that beset her. With minor differences her problems are shared by most of the men, women and children in Asia.

What of India today, and is her situation — one may ask — so very different from what it was, say, several centuries ago?

One retort to such a question might be to point out that a change has indeed taken place because India

* A description of the physical and climatic characteristics of Russia, including references to its agricultural lands and practices, is contained in Chapter VIII of the author's earlier book, *Our Plundered Planet.*

and Pakistan together now have as many people as there were in the entire world only three centuries ago. At this moment India's population is increasing at the staggering figure of not less than thirteen thousand every twenty-four hours. This country's present crisis is one of degree and not of kind. Her people have faced want and even starvation in times past, just as have other people in other countries throughout the world. Consequently any portrayal of India's present situation as being unprecedented would be false. The question of India, as of the world situation, is not "Has it happened before?" The effort in this dramatic and emerging period of civilization is to relieve suffering, not to extenuate it.

It may be revealing to glance at least briefly at some of the circumstances of India's more recent history and of her present situation. For a long time India was thought of as one of the richest countries in the world, with a land area — now divided into the states of India and Pakistan — of approximately a million and a half square miles. This is equivalent to more than one half the area of the United States and to four fifths that of Europe. Its endowment of natural resources was available to a population which, until the beginning of the nineteenth century, was approximately one quarter its present size. Limited facilities of transport isolated various regions one from another. Curiously enough, this circumstance had its favorable aspects in that disasters from epidemics tended to be localized.

At the time that India became a part of the British Empire in 1858, its population was about 175,000,000. In those days little was known of the prevention of infectious diseases other than smallpox. The work of the British was devoted principally to the establishment of law and order, increased production of food, industrial development and the improvement of transport facilities. One result of these efforts was a substantial improvement in the food situation; population growth remained slow because of the continued prevalence of epidemic diseases, although these commenced to diminish in the early days of the British regime with the introduction of rudimentary forms of public health measures.

The control of such major diseases as cholera and malaria began to be felt throughout the world during the middle or latter part of the last century, and it was at this time that the population of India commenced its great increase. In the last hundred years the Indian subcontinent has added considerably more than two hundred million people to its numbers.

It is frequently claimed that the solution to the Indian problem can be found through increasing agricultural production. It is pointed out that the average yield per acre of India's principal food grains is about one third that obtained in the United States. Consequently, it would seem that the introduction of modern agricultural methods, coupled with other agrarian reforms, can prove the road to deliverance. Unfortunately, many practical obstacles stand in the way. Much of the land is deficient in nitrogen and phosphate. Many regions are lacking in dependable water supply. The farmers in the great Southwest of the United States — in southern California, southern Colorado, New Mexico and Arizona — facing growing water shortages, will know just what that means. In West Bengal, one of India's richest agricultural regions, a recent survey by its Agricultural, Fisheries and Irrigation Departments states that the "natural drainage system and main source of natural irrigation are unmistakably dying." In East Bengal, due to deforestation and improper land practices on the watersheds, the ravages of floods are increasingly serious.

There is another obstacle that stands in the way of increasing land productivity, common not only to many parts of India but to other Asiatic as well as Near Eastern countries. Because of shortages or complete absence of wood, cow manure is molded into cakes, sun-dried, and then used as fuel. The loss to the soil of this natural organic fertilizer is incalculable.

The recital of difficulties becomes tiresome, but two others need to be mentioned. Both are the result of either religious or social customs. The former is the problem of the sacred cow, whose flesh cannot be eaten and whose utility as a "fuel producer" is more than off-set by the constant drain that such animals place on food supply that otherwise might be turned to human use. "Cow" is a misnomer in that the animals may be of either sex and the females, as a rule, are not in condition to produce milk. Actually the ordinary cow is not valued for milking in India. The female buffalo is preferred because of the greater richness of its milk. Another difficulty standing in the way of better agricultural results is that of the division of the land into smaller and smaller plots — so tiny often as to become virtually unworkable. This is due to inheritance customs which, in many regions, decree that a father having, let us say, three sons, should not merely divide his farm into three parts, leaving one to each, but should distribute his property by dividing his good land into three parts and, in turn, his medium and his poor land into three parts. With the steady and rapid increase in population, holdings in many regions have become constantly smaller and more widely scattered. As an old Indian, a retired British civil servant, observed but recently to an American newspaper correspondent, "Soon there will be more land in the ridges separating the fields than there is in the fields themselves."

Such are some of the difficulties standing in the way of agricultural betterment. It is not as if in the past much intelligent effort had not been applied to this end. For long centuries the people of India lived in reasonable balance with their land's productivity. Subsequently, the British in their time, as well as the Indian and Pakistan governments in recent years, had "Agricultural Development" at the top of their lists for action. But not until this century has the torrent of human multiplication so violently distorted the equation between people and the resources that sustain them. A population growth of the kind experienced in recent decades, and still continuing, would soon take up any conceivable agricultural improvement that could be made, even under the best of circumstances.

No one — other than a suffering native of India — can imagine what existing conditions mean to the people of the country. For instance, a report of the Health Survey and Development Committee published in 1946 states that "In the tenements constructed and owned by the Government of Bombay, 63,000 persons in 1939 were housed in 13,000 rooms," or almost five people per room. That was some years ago. A recent editorial in the *Statesman,* a leading newspaper of that city, states that "30% of the population of Bombay live with 20 or more people to a room." The city of Calcutta has more than four million people now compared with two million only five years ago; yet in this brief time there is little change in the number of houses or in facilities such as water supply or sewage disposal.

Conditions such as the above are only partly illustrative of the distress that, in one form or another, bears upon all the people, whether in the cities or the agricultural districts. In India's present difficulties, housing, even of the most primitive kind, becomes, in effect, a secondary matter. Two hundred thousand people in Calcutta, homeless and living on the streets, become but an incident in the total picture. How provide homes for thirteen thousand more people each day! Even America, with all its material resources, could barely do that. At this hour there is no ready answer to that problem; the nearer question is — will tens of millions starve? This time it threatens to be no local district famine as in the old days, nor an episode — if one dares to call it merely that — like the Bengal famine in 1943, which is estimated to have caused the death of two million or more people. This time the lives of tens of millions are in the balance. How could it be that humanity could allow itself to come to such a pass? Who has a right to criticize India? A large part of our world is moving slowly but inexorably to a similar crisis — avoidable if we so choose, but will we, in time?

The desperate exigency of India is forcing it to take steps that would have been unthought of even a quarter of a century ago. During World War II the Indian National Congress set up the National Planning Committee under the chairmanship of Pandit Nehru. Among the committee's resolutions is the following:

In the interests of social economy family happiness and national planning, family planning and a limitation of children are essential, and the State should adopt a policy to encourage these. It is desirable to lay stress on self-control, as well as to spread knowledge of cheap and safe methods of birth control. Birth control clinics should be established and other necessary measures taken in this behalf . . .

Subsequently, after India's freedom was finally established, the National Planning Commission under the chairmanship of the prime minister was created. Its first report, a five-year plan, was published in 1951 and carried the force of governmental authority. Among its measured statements, which touch so intimately upon many of the thoughts in this book, is the following:

In planning for a progressive improvement in living standards, the implications of . . . rapid growth of population need carefully to be considered. While it may be difficult to say what the optimum level of population for India should be and while it would also be wrong to underrate the potentialities of modern science and techniques to augment the productive capacity of the country, it is clear that, under present conditions, an increase in manpower "resources" does not strengthen the economy but, in fact, weakens it. The population problem is complex and it has several aspects, economic and social. It is necessary in the present context only to stress the fact that unless measures are initiated at this stage to bring down the birthrate and thereby to reduce the rate of population growth, a continuously increasing amount of effort on the part of the community will be used up only in maintaining existing standards of consumption. With all the effort that the First Five Year Plan will represent, it will be possible barely to restore by 1955–56 the pre-war standards of consumption in regard to essentials like food and clothing. Increasing pressure of population on natural resources (which must inevitably be limited) retards economic progress and limits seriously the rate of extension of social services, so essential to civilised existence. A population policy is, therefore, essential to planning.

It is a rather striking fact that two countries so far removed from each other, Sweden in the West and India in the East, are providing examples of leadership in dealing with this essential question of population. Within the turn of yet another quarter century it is a foregone conclusion that innumerable other countries will be joining with them.

IX. HORIZONS AND MIRAGES

*The possibilities of
additional resources — the
promise of science?*

THE PRESENT PERIOD through which the human race is passing might well be called "the era of revelations." The genii are at work. New discoveries, flowing one upon the other from the feverish laboratories of science, release undreamed of forces. Man is approaching the final threshold of knowledge of the physical world around him, and is even unlocking the ultimate secrets hidden within the infinities of space.

Can it be that we are really earth-bound? Must we admit, at the moment when the mind of man is unleashing the forces of nuclear energy, that the bodies of a billion human beings are enduring the agelong sufferings of hunger? What does the peasant in India or China say, or the Bantu in South Africa, the gleaner in the Amazon, the fellah in Egypt, the farmer in Calabria? What is nuclear energy to them?

So far, consideration has been given here solely to

the land itself. What of new and still untapped resources, or of new processes, which can help meet the ever-increasing world demand for the essentials of life? Surely the genii who have created the miracles in the physical sciences should somehow be able to provide for the more immediate needs of humanity.

Several prospects are being much talked about these days. One is that of tapping the immense reserves of organic material, both plant and animal, that exist in the ocean. Another is the manufacture of artificial foods. Then there are other possibilities that might advance the existing potentials of agriculture itself, including the inducement of rainfall and the conversion of sea water to fresh for the irrigation of regions at present too arid to bear crops.

It may well be that any one of these or similar potentialities may eventually prove of considerable importance to the human race. Consequently, the attempt will be made to measure a number of them in the light of present knowledge or of their present stages of development, weighing, as far as possible, the positives and negatives in each instance.

So, let us leave behind us, for a moment, the ideas and observations that have been expressed concerning some of the major land areas of our world and try to gain perspective regarding the degree to which additional resources may be counted upon, starting with those from the oceans.

MARINE RESOURCES

Fisheries

A good deal has been said and written lately about the oceans as "vast storehouses of unexploited wealth." A theme that keeps cropping up in discussions of world food problems is that even if the resources of land should become used to the extreme limits of their capacity, there is the enormous, virgin territory of the sea, full of food and minerals and who-knows-what-other mysterious riches to supply human needs of the future amply.

Probably the best way to commence is to refer first to some of the general conclusions that were reached at a recent world meeting on this subject. In 1949, the United Nations held a Scientific Conference on the Conservation and Utilization of Resources. There a number of fishery experts, representing many regions of the world, pooled their knowledge and experience regarding the location and importance of existing and latent fishery stocks. They introduced their discussions with these pertinent statistics.

The present world production of fish is about twenty million tons per year. Two thirds of this quantity is consumed as fresh or preserved fish, one third is manufactured into animal feeds, oils and other industrial products. Asia produces 49 per cent of the total quantity of fish caught, Europe 32 per cent, North America

16 per cent, the remaining parts of the world 3 per cent. Production is distributed among the oceans thus: Pacific, 48 per cent, Atlantic, 47 per cent; Indian, 5 per cent. Of the total catch, 98 per cent is taken in the Northern Hemisphere, 2 per cent in the Southern Hemisphere. Only 2 per cent of the number of known species of sea fishes compose 90 per cent of the world's catch. Herrings and their relatives compose almost half of that.

After thus taking inventory of the fishes that the oceans now yield, the conferees marked on a chart the places where they believed important new fisheries could be developed or where well-established fisheries could be expanded. (Their estimates did not take into account possible increases by U.S.S.R. fisheries, on which data were not available.) They agreed that production could be increased by approximately three million tons in temperate zones, and by half that amount in the tropics, or a total increase of about one quarter over present yields. This would indicate a possible world production of fish aggregating approximately twenty-five million tons per year. For anyone caring for relatively meaningless statistics this would mean that about four hundred million people could have about one third of a pound of fish a day. In any case, the various preceding figures provide some idea of the extent to which this source of food contributes to human diet at the present time.

Since the 1949 meeting, new knowledge has been gained, thanks to exploratory researches going on in various parts of the world. It appears that pilchard, a species of herring, are not so abundant south of Australia as had been supposed. (Shakespeare was not an ichthyologist but he remarked that "fools are as like husbands as pilchards are to herrings"!) On the other hand, American biologists, working out of Hawaii, have discovered very promising tuna stocks occupying a band along the counterequatorial current in the mid-Pacific. Other Americans working out of Seattle have reported large quantities of redfish, flatfish and sablefish in the North Pacific, and flatfish, cod and pollack in the Bering Sea.

Of all forms of fishing, trawling is one of the most productive, and one of the most promising for new fisheries. The earliest trawls were simply conical bags of netting dragged over the bottom by sailboats and held open at the mouth by a wooden beam. In modern trawls, two otter boards, or doors, are hung from the towing ropes in such a way that the force of the sea water pushing against their slanted surfaces holds the net open. Adoption of this device permitted the use of much larger nets than did the beam trawl, and resulted in a tremendous increase in the catch of bottom-living fishes.

The major trawling areas of the world, the Baltic and North Sea banks, the New England banks and the

Grand Banks of Newfoundland are famous in history. In more recent years trawling has been extended to the Arctic Ocean and to the Pacific Coast of the United States and Canada. In spite of these advances to new territory, however, there are still proved trawling grounds that are practically untouched. Three of such regions are worth some discussion in order to throw light upon the conditions that will influence their development. All three of these regions are located in the Pacific and adjacent seas, and all are well documented with records of the fish and shellfish available. They are the Bering Sea, the deep grounds off the coast of the state of Washington, and the waters surrounding the Philippine Islands.

True, some of these new areas are farther from established markets than the ones presently being fished. It is probable, however, that the long-term trend of food prices will be upward. Furthermore, new methods of getting sea foods to market are being constantly developed and improved. These two trends, probable rising prices and improved preservation-in-transit techniques, should bring new areas into the commercially feasible range year by year. The history of the exploration of these areas is interesting enough and the findings are significant enough to follow in some detail.

When Peter the Great commissioned the famous navigator Vitus Bering to explore the west coast of what is now Alaska, he opened the way to developments which still have not been completed. The first voyage, in 1725, revealed the expanse of the Bering Sea as the ships crossed from Okhotsk to Bering Strait and returned.

In Bering's time the chief interest was in the land surrounding his sea rather than in the sea itself. Exploitation by the Russians of the fur resources relegated the sea to a place merely for the passage of ships. By the end of the nineteenth century, however, Japan, faced with a population needing food far beyond its agricultural resources, looked to this northern sea. Its exploitation of the crab resources was successful, and continued on a large scale until interrupted by World War II.

From a fishery point of view, the Bering Sea looks like a treasure trove, as indeed it is. Of its 878,000 square miles, 42 per cent is less than a hundred fathoms deep — ideal for trawling. Hence, this tremendous shallow basin may well one day become one of the world's major trawling areas. Although the surrounding areas are sparsely populated, new methods of processing and transportation will bring the markets of the United States and Canada within reach.

In 1941 the United States Fish and Wildlife Service started exploring the Bering Sea with an expedition which was to be primarily for the large king crabs known to be abundant there. Since floating canneries had been successfully used by the Japanese, one of these was outfitted, and sailed from Seattle in August, accompanied by a fishing vessel. This expedition was followed by another in the following spring.

These expeditions were phenomenally successful in spite of the fact that they did not confine themselves to areas of greatest abundance. They caught crabs at the rate of 80 per hour in 213 hauls scattered over 100,000 square miles of sea. This was encouraging, since crabs were the primary objective; but even more surprising were the quantities of fish which they took incidentally. In the 213 hauls for crab, they took, at the same time, 30 cod per hour, and found other species to be even more abundant. A group of 240 hauls with otter trawl yielded an average of 2000 pounds of flounder per haul. The size of these catches becomes evident when compared with those of the commercially successful trawl fishery in Puget Sound, which operates on an average take of 500 pounds per haul.

After the war, in 1947, exploration of the Bering Sea was resumed, with a voyage of the hundred-foot refrigerated steel trawler *Alaska*. This vessel employed a North Atlantic trawl, about a hundred feet wide. It fished an area fifty miles long and sixty miles offshore near the outer portion of Bristol Bay. Again the results were impressive. In thirty-six days during June and July, 14,000 crabs were caught, which yielded 50,000 pounds of meat. In addition to the crabs the following quantities of fish were taken in 148 hauls: 105,000 pounds of flounder, 45,000 pounds of cod, 38,000 pounds of pollack.

The results of these and two subsequent expeditions prove that the Bering Sea can produce fish and crabs — large quantities of them. They also indicate what must be done to harvest the resource successfully and bring it to market.

The land surrounding the sea is very sparsely settled, and only Anchorage, Alaska, could be considered a market; this city of eleven thousand people obviously could not absorb any great part of the catch of a modern fishery. A possible headquarters for a fishery would be Dutch Harbor, in the Aleutian chain. From there it is 1707 miles to Seattle and 2040 miles to Honolulu. These distances require that the catch be preserved in some way and the best way now known is refrigeration. With modern equipment it is possible to freeze an entire fare of crab and flatfish at sea and take it to market even over these tremendous distances. Furthermore, the fish on arriving at the market can be thawed, filleted, and the fillets refrozen in salable condition.

The fisherman or fishing company considering expansion into the Bering Sea must make a clear-eyed appraisal of the advantages and disadvantages. The one great advantage, which by itself must ultimately outweigh all disadvantages, is the proven, located abundance of crabs and flatfish. The exploratory work has demonstrated a rich abundance of these species, the latter as much as four times as great as in areas now supporting commercial fisheries. The disadvantages can be summarized as follows:

1. *Weather:* Extremely high winds and heavy seas are characteristic of the area, and only the most seaworthy boats can be operated. The northern part is closed by ice from October to May and the southern part from December to April, so that the fishing season can only be from four to seven months long.

2. *Distance from markets:* Seattle and Honolulu, the nearest markets of any size, are each about two thousand miles away.

3. *Quality of flatfish:* Some of the flatfish taken were reported to be of small size and inferior quality. This may be an effect of crowding which would be corrected when and if fishing thins out the stocks of fish.

Each of these disadvantages can be overcome, and will be when necessary effort is turned to the job. Adverse weather can be met by using the right type of vessel at the right time of year, distance to market by the proper refrigeration of the catch, and poor quality by trawling the grounds to reduce overcrowding. The disadvantages have so far served to discourage the development of these fishing grounds, which is now limited merely to one cod-fishing schooner and one refrigerated trawler catching king crabs. American enterprise has moved into difficult fields before, however, and it can do it again.

The second area is somewhat closer to existing markets than the Bering Sea. It lies off the coast of the state of Washington beyond present trawling depths. In 1951 the exploratory vessel *John N. Cobb* fished an area sixty miles from north to south and fifty-five miles offshore, lying outside the northern end of the state and the Strait of Juan de Fuca. The standard West Coast type of trawl was used, and commercial quantities of fish were found in depths of from 100 to 225 fathoms.

The principal species taken in the course of sixty-one hauls were Dover sole, sablefish and Pacific Ocean perch, all of which are marketable. Over large areas the following quantities were taken per hour of trawling: Pacific Ocean perch, 1000 pounds; sablefish, 500 pounds; Dover sole, 1000 pounds. These quantities are ample to support a commercial operation. The only addition required to standard trawling equipment now in use on the West Coast would be longer trawling wires. Fishing experience on the *Cobb* proved that five hundred fathoms of wire would be sufficient for all of the grounds covered during its voyage.

Finally, as regards the waters around the Philippine Islands, the United States Government explored trawling grounds there after the Second World War as a measure to stimulate new fishing industries and to improve the Islands' food supply. Two vessels, working over the area thoroughly, took an average of 151 pounds of fish in an hour. They caught a great variety of tropical species, none of them anywhere near as abundant as the fish one finds in the northern seas. If those results are characteristic of the tropics, as they appear to be, it seems doubtful that trawling in that part of the Pacific can pay well enough to develop into important fishing industries.

A major lesson to be learned is that methods which are successful in one part of the world are not necessarily so elsewhere. Gear that pays off handsomely in the United States or in Europe might fail dismally, or be prohibitively expensive, in less industrialized countries. It might be all right for fishing dense populations of a single species, like cod, but all wrong for mixed stocks with different aggregation habits.

Undoubtedly the greatest contribution that could be made towards increasing the use of marine fish everywhere is to carry on a variety of industrial and biological researches to find ways of significantly reducing the cost and of improving the attractiveness of fishery products. Until that is accomplished, there is slight reason to anticipate any startling increases in the supplies to be gained from marine fisheries.

Plankton

A vast assemblage of different kinds of creatures drift with the currents of the sea, composing a kind of community of communities called "the plankton." Here are swarms of microscopic plants and animals and a great variety of crustaceans, jellyfishes, sea combs and worms — in fact representatives of almost every known group of invertebrate animals. There is also a variety of exotic fishes living in the community. Most of the animals in the plankton are not completely passive, but their movements are slow enough so that one can catch quantities by simply towing a cloth net through the water.

Although plankton is universal in the sea, it is by no means uniformly distributed. It is most abundant in places where the surface water is enriched from below by such processes as upwelling, tidal action or seasonal changes in temperature — in other words, over or near continental shelves and in certain parts of the open sea, as near the equator, where two great adjacent currents flow in opposite directions. Whatever its abundance, the plankton concentrates more or less in layers, which make vertical migrations — towards the surface about sunset, away from the surface into deeper water about sunrise. These layers make very distinct traces on echo-sounding instruments, which seem too pronounced to be accounted for by the quantities which ordinary plankton nets catch. Consequently, there is a growing suspicion that plankton is denser than had once been supposed and may contain organisms which no one has yet succeeded in sampling. Oceanographers are puzzling very much over the composition of these deep, scattering layers, speculating as to whether they are predominantly of squid, fish, shrimp or something yet unknown.

There is far more organic matter bound up in the plankton than in the few species of fishes which we eat. Why not harvest the plankton directly? It is more abundant near shore than off shore, and it concentrates near the surface during part of the twenty-four hours. Therefore it is accessible. It is nutritious. About 50 to 60 per cent of it is protein, 5 to 15 per cent fat, around 15 per cent carbohydrate. It is rich in minerals and vitamins. People have eaten it. Along the coast of China a paste made from the shrimplike constituents of plankton is a culinary staple; in Scandinavia, people eat certain small crustaceans. The crew of the *Kon-Tiki* ate considerable amounts of plankton and found it palatable and hunger-satisfying. Scientists on recent expeditions, when studying the possible use of plankton as a survival ration for men stranded in life rafts at sea, ate a quarter to a half pound of plankton a day and suffered no ill consequences. They say the taste reminded them of shrimps or raw oysters.

No matter how delicious plankton may be, it is unlikely that people generally will very readily accept it as a regular article of diet. If we are going to be realistic about the commercial development of supplies of plankton, we had probably better think in terms of converting it to beef, pork, poultry, eggs, cheese and butter, in effect, by using it in animal feeds. This would mean making it into meal. There would undoubtedly be some valuable by-products, like condensed nutrient solubles, oils, amino acids, and perhaps other substances yet to be discovered.

There is a well-established market for animal-feed meals made of sea products. For example, more than a thousand tons of shrimp meal were sold in the Gulf States in 1949 at an average price of ninety dollars per ton. This product is made from scrap left over when the shrimp are prepared for the market. A meal made from whole plankton should be of at least equal value.

If there is such great potential value in the plankton, why is it not now being exploited? Because no one has yet demonstrated how to catch it properly. Efforts have been made, including some in recent years by skilled engineers, but as yet no process has been devised and is now operating that is practical and successful. Here is a challenge to engineers with an interest in the sea, some knowledge of biology and a feeling for the material needs of mankind.

Herring, mackerel, menhaden, porpoises and whales are wonderfully efficient in collecting plankton. The blue whale, within even five years, grows to a length of seventy feet or more and a weight estimated to be in excess of a hundred tons on a diet of plankton. We have not learned how to compete with those animals in their own environment.

Seaweeds

It is very hard in studying scientific literature on sea-weeds to reach a definitive opinion about their value for human beings. In the opinion of some authorities they are a woefully neglected, great potential source of food and industrial raw material. In the opinion of others, they have very limited uses and are too costly to harvest and dry to ever be available for cheap, mass-production processes. They are certainly abundant in some parts of the world. Nobody can fly along the Pacific Coast of North or South America without being deeply impressed by the band of giant kelp that parallels the shores. Between western Alaska and northern Baja California, there are 390 square miles of kelp beds, estimated to contain about sixty million tons of plants. There is probably a similar amount in South America, something like seventeen million tons in the Falkland Islands, half a million tons in Tasmania, fifty thousand tons in New Zealand. And there are unestimated quantities of other sorts of brown algae and red algae widely distributed around the shores throughout the world.

Scientists classify seaweeds, according to their characteristic colors, into four groups, the blue, green, red, and brown algae. Only two of these are commercially valuable, the red and the brown. Although they are widely distributed geographically, they reach their greatest development and density in temperate and cold climates. While we are familiar with those species that border the shores of populated places like Norway, Great Britain, New England, California, Hawaii, Japan and Chile, very little is known about their occurrence or extent in remote areas, especially in the arctic and antarctic, where, according to reports of explorers, dense underwater forests of large marine algae have been discovered.

In most maritime countries, particularly in the Orient and Oceania, people eat seaweeds — some species for vegetables, others for condiments, still others in sweet preparations. Unfortunately, neither the carbohydrates nor the proteins in seaweeds yield to human digestion, and must therefore serve chiefly as bulk. The nutritional value of seaweeds lies almost wholly in their content of minerals — including some of the trace elements — and in their vitamins, which vary in quantity and assortment from species to species and from season to season.

Seaweeds are useful as supplemental food for animals. Ruminants such as sheep and cattle are able to digest their carbohydrates, and when pasturing along the seashore browse on seaweeds, sometimes in preference to land-grown plants. The addition of 5 to 10 per cent of dried seaweed to feed rations is said to strengthen disease resistance in stock, to improve milk production in cows and laying capacity in poultry.

The organic matter, the mineral content and the colloidal properties of seaweeds also give them value as fertilizers and soil conditioners. They have been so used in the Old World since ancient times.

Plant physiologists are giving a great deal of attention to the experimental cultivation of marine as well as fresh-water microscopic algae like Chlorella and Scenedesmus to penetrate the mysteries of photosynthesis; by modifying the illumination and the composition of salts in the water, they can control the carbohydrate, fat and protein content of these plants. This artificial cultivation is now prohibitively expensive; yet sometime in the very distant future, researchers may discover how to bring production costs down to levels where mass production would be economically feasible. Meanwhile it has transpired from these botanical researches that some of the algae have an antibiotic effect. How this might in itself become useful to man for controlling diseases and for food preservation remains yet to be developed.

It is true that seaweed resources are not nearly fully exploited now. But they are probably exploited almost or quite up to the limit of demand. Meanwhile, botanists, chemists and other scientists are working in a number of laboratories, mostly in Europe, searching for new uses of seaweeds and for means of overcoming the severe difficulties of harvesting and drying.

Pond culture

There are untold stretches of salty wasteland bordering shores all over the world. Places like mangrove swamps, salt-water marshes, salt flats, which are not fit as they are for any agricultural purpose or much else, for that matter, often lie quite neglected. That is a pity, for they can be made to yield very profitable quantities of food, as has been well demonstrated in many parts of the Orient where brackish- and salt-water fish farming is an old art. Statistics on this subject are fragmentary, but a few figures have been published which suggest that the potentialities of such culture might be very substantial. In Hong Kong, for example, there are brackish ponds which, by the most knowledgeable cultivation, produce as much as 3000 pounds of fish annually per acre. Elsewhere, yields are considerably lower, nevertheless good. In Formosa, some 24,000 acres of ponds, which are harder to manage because they are considerably more saline than those in Hong Kong, produce an average of about 660 pounds per acre. Along the north coast of Java and in South Celebes, 250,000 acres have been developed not only for growing fish (20,000 to 25,000 tons annually) but also for mangrove trees, which are planted along the dykes and which furnish wood. In the Philippines, 175,000 acres of brackish ponds are cultivated to produce annually 25,000 tons worth around $17,000,000.

Even in these countries where salt-water pond culture is practiced, very large tracts of swamps remain undeveloped. In the Philippines alone, for example, there are close to a million acres of such neglected swampland. A reason for this neglect is that the initial investment required to convert a salt-water marsh to fish-culture purposes is costly enough to be beyond the reach of most prospective fish farmers. In Indonesia for example, this conversion cost amounts to five or six hundred dollars an acre. The annual yield there being two hundred to five hundred pounds, such a capital investment is far higher than is required for ordinary sea fishing. Yet, in the long run, it probably pays better because it is a safer investment. The yield sometimes decreases after a few years of operation. This was the experience in Bengal. But there, aquatic scientists, after studying the situation, concluded that the declining productivity resulted from increasing salinity, and it was only necessary to gain access to fresh water to restore the yields to their former value. Another reason for neglecting the shore wasteland is that local residents are often not familiar with salt-water fish farming, and being conservative, they resist anything so novel. If capital is available they must first be convinced that this is a good way to use it, and afterward they must be taught the special techniques involved in fish farming. All this must be accomplished, under favorable circumstances, by setting up demonstration centers and operating them for profit as well as education.

One of the two or three most widely used species for brackish-water fish farming is the milkfish (*Chanos chanos*). This wondrously silver relative of the herrings lives in the warm waters of the Pacific and Indian Oceans, from southern California to Panama, from Japan to Australia to the Red Sea. It is ideally suited for cultivation because it is completely vegetarian and therefore does not attack other fishes or its own kind. It feeds on algae, which can grow in enormous quantities in ponds under favorable conditions. It is remarkably hardy. It is highly prolific, producing from three to five million eggs per spawning. The eggs hatch along the shore, and the fry are consequently easily available to fishermen, who gather them up to be transplanted to the ponds. Even the fry are hardy. They are transported in earthenware jars of twenty- to thirty-quart capacity sometimes more than five hundred miles. They grow remarkably fast, so that it is possible to harvest one to three times from the same pond in a year. Milkfish are usually marketed when they weigh about a pound. At that size they bring the best price. Smaller fish, six or seven to the pound, are less desirable and are sold to the poorer trade.

Ponds are constructed to take advantage of the tide, so that the water is being continually changed. The incoming water carries with it, among other things, very young prawns. These animals characteristically drift into the rich water of the swamps, where they spend their young stages. Thus those that get into the ponds grow there, and when it comes time for their seaward migration they get caught in the traps which the fish farmers have installed for that purpose. The young of various species of fishes also drift into the ponds with the incoming tides. Among these are mullet, which are slow-growing vegetarians, and also predatory fishes, like *Lates,* which are a nuisance because they feed on milkfish and prawns. Crabs get into the ponds, too; they are very good for food, but very damaging to the dykes. By proper construction of the ponds, farmers can keep out predatory and otherwise harmful species; and by proper management they can improve the productivity of their ponds and the profits therefrom. At least brief mention should be made here of the fact that in addition to salt-water or tidal ponds there are distinct possibilities in fresh-water pond culture. In India, Palestine and elsewhere, fresh-water ponds are being put to good use.

People working in the Food and Agriculture Organization of the United Nations and in other agencies devoted to raising standards of living give much attention to promoting pond culture, for they believe this to be one of the most important potential sources of protein. However, their facilities and staffs are small compared to the areas of need. Moreover, such resistances as conservatism, superstition, apathy, suspicion and downright hostility to strangers yield very slowly and only to the most artful approaches. That takes the labors of a very special quality of educator, of whom there are precious few. Here, then, is an opportunity for young men willing to submit themselves to a rigorous education in the sciences and the humanities, looking for a life of service and self-dedication.

SUPPLEMENTS TO FOOD–SUPPLY, AND OTHER TECHNICAL DEVELOPMENTS

There is good reason to believe that a number of new processes, in various stages of development at the present time, will eventually add to the world's potential food supply. In few fields of endeavor have recent advances been more spectacular than in the field of applied chemistry, and notably in the realm of synthetics.

Many of these achievements, however, have been considerably exaggerated by science-fiction reporters, who successfully peddle their wares to the headline-hungry press and magazine trade. Undoubtedly there will be a continuing flow of such misleading material. Regrettably, it is necessary to be equally wary of the inveterate laboratory optimist who, disregarding all economic and social ramifications, airily leaps the gulf between the test tube and the realities of mass production.

Current literature is replete with statements and comments on the impact of this or that discovery, but it is also filled with contradictions as to the practical applicability or the eventual date of a new product's or process's commercial usability. Such contradictions are to be expected, for most of the synthetic foods under discussion have not yet outgrown the experimental stage, let alone the pilot, or demonstration, plant stage.

In the following paragraphs some of the researches now under way will be examined without any attempt to evaluate them or predict their ultimate importance. It would be well to begin with a brief reference to chemistry in agriculture, a field in which some of the most concrete and proven advances have been made to date.

The recent discovery of a soil conditioner has aroused considerable interest among scientists and laymen alike. This soil conditioner, which, incidentally, merely improves the physical condition, or *structure,* of a soil and not its fertility, is now sold commercially under a number of trade names. It is destined to become a valuable aid to farmer and gardener alike, for it loosens the hardest and cakiest soils and produces a granular, friable structure which facilitates plant growth and simultaneously reduces the danger of erosion by inhibiting runoff. Since, unlike organic compounds, the ingredients of the conditioner (sodium salts of hydrolyzed polyacrylonitrile) are not subject to bacterial decomposition, their aggregating strength is retained for longer periods of time, thus obviating the need for frequent applications. Having passed the laboratory as well as the field tests with flying colors, the new soil conditioner still faces the price barrier. Accessible to the gardener and the intensive truck farmer, Krilium (one of the new trade names) remains too expensive for large-scale application. This product requires extremely large amounts of raw materials and, for the present, it is an open question whether it can be manufactured in quantities sufficient for widespread distribution. In any event it still remains for the industrial engineer to devise mass-production techniques which will bring the demonstrated benefits of the soil conditioner to the farmer of our own interior lowlands as well as, finally, to the millions of marginal peasants throughout the world.

At least as important as good structure is the soil's content of essential nutrients. Chemical agriculture is making impressive headway in the task of maintaining the soil's mineral balance.* Soils are constantly being leached of their more soluble salts, especially when under constant cultivation. One of the ways through which these minerals can be restored to the soil is with the help of marine algae and waste products of the fishing industry. Thus, the commercial distribution of trace minerals recovered from the sea — the possibilities

* Francis Joseph Weiss, "Chemical Agriculture," *Scientific American*, August 1952, p. 16.

of which have been spoken of in the preceding pages — would greatly benefit those farming lands suffering from excessive leaching. Such trace minerals, if available in quantity, would be capable of providing a much needed supplement to the action of bulk minerals in the commercial fertilizers now in use.

Any discussion of synthetic foods *proper* must deal at the very outset with a common and all-pervasive prejudice — namely, the feeling that natural foods are better and more wholesome than artificial ones. We are all very much concerned with the appearance and the taste of our everyday meals, and the chemist studying new processes must be sensitive to peoples' habits and desires. There is an old German saying to the effect that whatever the peasant does not know, he will not eat. During the immediate postwar shortage in Europe, people very generally refused to add corn to their diet, although ample supplies of that crop were available at the time. This illustrates how a new food, one made from yeast for example, would lie on the shelves of the grocers unless, through one means or another, the buying public were attracted to it and really wished to make a practice of using it. It is almost axiomatic that the poorer and the more backward people are, the more distrustful they are of any innovations in their way of life. There have been a number of instances of how difficult it is to introduce fish into the diet of chronically underfed countries whose coastal waters abound in hitherto unused marine life. Elaborate allowance, too, must be made for those other "prejudices" which are the result of traditional or religious objections to certain foods or of aversions to certain methods or ingredients used in their preparation.

In producing artificial foods the chemist is concerned with synthesizing all or part of the three great ingredients which make up our natural foods: carbohydrates, fats, proteins. One way of synthesizing is to imitate the operation performed by the plant. Plants employ the energy of the sun to transform the carbon dioxide in the atmosphere into energy-bearing foodstuffs. This process is known as photosynthesis, and a great deal of research is now being directed at solving the riddle of that transformation. As recently as November 23, 1952, the *New York Times* reported that research at the University of California had penetrated the mystery of how the energy of sunlight enters into the chemistry of the plant. If this discovery is substantiated and confirmed — and there is no reason to believe it may not be — it would indicate that a point has been reached where the whole photosynthetic process can be controlled in simple water organisms like algae. Even prior to this report, ways had been discovered of forcing such humble and highly inedible organisms as algae to produce quantities of fats, proteins, or carbohydrates.

The most promising organism found thus far for

this operation is the green alga Chlorella, which can be grown in huge tanks or plastic cylinders on minerals and gas mixtures under optimum photosynthetic conditions (this plant multiplies at a rate that appears to be limited only by the carbon dioxide content of the water). Consequently, it has been found that algae in pans of water six inches deep are capable of absorbing up to 2 per cent of the total solar energy falling on a given area, as compared with less than 1 per cent for average agriculture. Also under laboratory conditions, yields equal to fifteen dry tons per acre have been realized; this is nearly five times the yield of the best land growth, and scientists believe that even this figure could be trebled. The Carnegie Institution has just reported on the results of the first pilot-plant operations with Chlorella.* These results indicate that large-scale culture of algae is technically feasible today. Nearly a hundred pounds of Chlorella were grown and then studied for their nutritive properties and possible application as industrial raw material. A detailed cost estimate reveals that the eventual cost of commercial production of the dry product might amount to less than ten cents per pound. In view of the high protein content of dried algae (close to 50 per cent) and their high vitamin potency, this cost of production

---

* John S. Burlew (editor), *Algal Culture: From Laboratory to Pilot Plant*. Publication No. 600, Carnegie Institution of Washington, D.C., July 1953.

seems low enough to warrant further investigations, this time on the scale of a demonstration plant growing algae on an area of about one acre. Such a plant, the Carnegie Institution's report claims, would be large enough to give operating experience on which the design of a commercial unit could be based; and also it would provide enough algae for *experiments on processing it as a food*. The last phrase has been emphasized because it indicates the wide gulf which still separates laboratory experiment from industrial process. It also shows how uncertain is the future of even those synthetic products which have been widely advertised as the solution for the food-population problem. This opinion is reinforced by the balanced words of Dr. Roger Adams in his presidential address in 1951 before the American Association for the Advancement of Science, when he stated: "Whether these algae may be used directly for cattle or human food, or whether they may be converted more profitably into chemicals or fuel, is a problem for the future." * Thus Dr. Adams, conscious of the difficulties yet to be encountered in devising methods of large-scale production, refrains from definitely predicting that Chlorella will ever be available and usable for human consumption.

Long before Chlorella or its derivatives may become part of our regular diet, it is likely that many of us

* Roger Adams, "Man's Synthetic Future," *Science*, February 15, 1952, p. 159.

will be partaking of another important source of proteins by way of yeasts. While nature sharply restricts the amount of protein that can be raised on one acre of land, she has set a generous limit on the production of carbohydrates. With this in mind, scientists have found that certain kinds of yeasts can turn carbohydrates into true protein fully as nutritious as beef. Biologists and engineers in the service of the sugar industry have been making substantial use of this circumstance. Pilot plants operated by sugar producers in Hawaii, Jamaica, the Union of South Africa, and Australia have already produced food yeasts from sugarcane juice plus added minerals. The idea is catching on in other sugar-growing areas. By projecting known results to large-scale operation, it may become possible to produce sufficient carbohydrate on one acre of irrigated and well-fertilized cane land to satisfy the annual protein need of approximately two hundred and fifty people. By way of comparison, one acre yielding twenty bushels of wheat fills the need of but three persons.

The yeast factory in Jamaica deserves special consideration, because in that overcrowded island the population has accepted yeast foods in such forms as porridges and fish cakes. Jamaica's output travels as far as England, where yeast is being increasingly used to enrich canned products with added protein.

Coming back to the more conventional sources of protein, we find that chemistry is also lending a helping hand to increase and improve the supply of meat animals. Artificial insemination, assisted by chemistry, is one example. Today more than 90 per cent of the dairy cows in the United States are artificially inseminated. Through proper dilution of semen, a good sire can serve fifty to a hundred times as many cows as would be possible in natural matings.* And chemistry is constantly improving formulas for diluters and helping to extend artificial insemination to ever more kinds of animals.

In regard to the feeding of young mammals, some forward-looking experiments are now under way. Until fairly recently it was taken for granted that mother milk was essential to keep the offspring alive. As a result, millions of farm animals, especially pigs and lambs, were being lost every year because of insufficient natural milk or because of accidents in the course of suckling. Even in the United States, where many modern practices have been introduced on farms, it has been estimated that up to 30 per cent of all pigs born fail to mature. In order to counter this waste, scientists are developing synthetic milk, composed of mixtures of protein, amino acids, vitamins and minerals,

* Francis Joseph Weiss, "Chemical Agriculture," *Scientific American*, August 1952, p. 18.

and fortified with growth-assisting antibiotics. This synthetic milk has proved to be more nourishing than the natural product, especially in the case of pigs. Piglets raised on this artificial food weigh as much as fifty pounds at the end of the normal nursing period instead of the usual twenty-two pounds, and they appear to be generally healthier. At the same time, sows are ready for a new mating almost immediately after they have borne a litter.

One of the most interesting points in this whole development is that artificial milk contains what used to be noxious waste products of the fishing industry. The water fraction resulting from the steam-processing of menhaden (for fertilizer) is commonly called "stick water." It contains many valuable minerals, water-soluble proteins, amino acids and vitamins. Until World War II, fish processors overlooked the nutritive value of this waste material, and it was not until they were forced to do something about the public nuisance of their sewage that they began to recover fish solubles by centrifuging, vacuum evaporation, and condensation. These materials are now a rich source of the growth-producing vitamin B_{12}, and constitute an ideal base for synthetic milk.

The above sequence is a striking example of how pollution control and conservation measures were happily combined to further scientific investigation and resulted in the discovery of ways to increase food supply.

Other scientific developments now on the horizon must be mentioned. These deal with man's attempt to shape major environmental forces.

Water, or rather the lack of it, more than any other factor, has limited development of lands for man's use. For several thousand years water has been moved from its place of natural occurrence through the use of irrigation systems. But vast areas remain where limited rainfall and stream flow prevent intensive use of land. Today new scientific concepts may perhaps open the way for man's controlling at least part of his environment in a much more sweeping way than that of diverting streams, or of felling forest to adapt the land to other uses.

Thousands of American farmers and ranchers within recent years have been contracting annually for the delivery of induced rainfall; even municipalities have been experimenting with the process. Several years ago, for example, the city of New York employed a "rain maker" for months during a period of serious water shortage, as has the city of Dallas more recently. Do we know what economic or even strategic military changes may lie in the scientific investigations of cloud seeding? Can we influence air-mass movements, and make more intense use possible of much of the world's ten million square miles which now have less than ten inches of rain a year? If any significant portion of these regions — one sixth of the earth's total land area —

could obtain a more even distribution of rain during a year, or a moderate increase, major changes in man's land use might follow.

Scientific investigation of short- and long-range weather control is in its infancy. Legal and economic as well as technical problems present barriers to such developments. But we are at a scientific threshold of possible great consequence.

Fascinating as this prospect may be, there are limitations inherent in the vagaries of nature. There is, for instance, no reason to believe that man-made rain would not vary from place to place as does natural precipitation. Generally, man requires water in adequate amounts at specific locations to meet the demands of his own concentrated creations — the cities, the factories, and the intensive agriculture which supports them.

Another area of scientific enquiry is the conversion of salt water to fresh. The oceans, the chief sources of our natural rainfall, lie near many man-made concentrations. Ever since Aristotle's time, men have thought to use sea water in some way to meet directly their needs for fresh water. Such water is now available — but at a cost. Ships at sea, remote islands, desert frontiers may have it at a price from ten to fifty times what it costs in normal circumstances.

Can fresh water be drawn and converted directly from the sea for widespread use and in large quantities? The most recent technical studies on this subject indicate little likelihood of this. Under any now known system, power costs *alone* would amount to more than most agricultural water sells for, and half of what much domestic and industrial water is delivered for. Thus, for large-scale use, there is at the present time no tangible promise of major developments. Even with free power, let us say from the sun, the capital costs and maintenance seem to make all methods uneconomic.

However, where brackish water is involved, where relatively small amounts are needed, and where relatively high prices — say twice those that are usual can be paid — new techniques involving such processes as ion exchange membranes offer a bright prospect. Here again science can offer at least some assistance in improving man's environment. Yet, the first task of science is to endeavor to fill the constantly widening gap between existing populations and their essential needs. As and when this is accomplished, it will be time to measure the capacity of new technologies to provide for the still greater demands of ever-increasing human numbers.

X. THE HOUR OF DECISION

*For now, as we
look, we can see
the limits of the earth*

Someone, sometime, somewhere ended a book
with a "Conclusion." This idea had its drawbacks but
it became a custom, and as Plutarch remarked, "We
are more sensible of what is done against custom than
against nature."

There can be no such thing as a *conclusion* in any
book that treats of human affairs and problems, because we strange beings, we people, do the most unexpected things and are capable of adapting ourselves
in unforeseeable ways to new circumstances. Beyond
that, no book, or innumerable series of books, could
anticipate all the factors that may have a bearing upon
the future of human life upon this earth. More than
once, in writing these pages, there has been great en-
ticement to deal less with material or physical matters
and more with the many exciting elements, intellectual
and moral, that make human life what it is — and
what it may be. We must have faith that humanity
will triumph in the end in reaching its incomparable

destiny. But always in speculating regarding the ultimate, one is drawn inexorably to consideration of the immediate, of the first need of all needs, of the means towards the barest living, of the question of minimal survival — adequacy of food and of other essential natural resources.

We are under the power of a timeless principle, exerting its influence relentlessly on a global scale. This principle is closely related to the law of supply and demand. It finds expression in a simple ratio wherein the numerator can be defined as "resources of the earth" and the denominator as "numbers of people." The numerator is *relatively* fixed and only partially subject to control by man. The denominator is subject to substantial change and is largely, if not entirely, subject to control by man. If we are blind to this law, or delude ourselves into minimizing its power, of one thing we can be assured — the human race will enter into days of increasing trouble, conflict and darkness.

How is one justified in giving as categorical an opinion as this regarding the future, even though it concerns a trend and not a finality? Presumably the best response is to sum up the reasons that appear to justify it and in doing so search for courses of action that would ward off a future so unnecessary and so dismal.

In view of the fact that the denominator of this timeless principle, namely, numbers of people, is to the greater degree subject to control by man, let's commence with a review of the general facts of population growth, making sure to consider them through the perspective of recent history.

Three hundred years ago, or in the middle of the seventeenth century, the earth's population is estimated to have been approximately 470,000,000 people, or about one fifth of today's number. There are various valid reasons for assuming that it had not previously much exceeded that number. However, the eighteenth century proved to be a period of major change. It witnessed the beginnings of better means of communication and transport, the introduction of the steam engine and an incipient improvement in medical care. It was a time of stirring, of new impulses, of breaking away from the prolonged era of medievalism. The revelation of new land and wealth in the Western Hemisphere had a profound psychological effect upon the minds of men. The earth was a vast place, after all. The fascination of new horizons galvanized the thoughts of European peoples. In a material sense this New World soon began to contribute to the welfare of Europe. At the same time the Far East shared in some degree these new influences. In effect the eighteenth century was a growing period — the dawn of the industrial revolution. As a consequence of these various encouraging influences, the population of the world increased by about 400,000,000 people in a century and a half, and at the opening of the nineteenth century had risen to about 870,000,000 people.

Then there came, at a steadily accelerating rate, the explosive increase in human numbers. The new forces of industrial production, the extension of commerce, of rapid transport of food and other materials and, above all, the revolutionary advances in the medical sciences spread their influences throughout the world. From the point of view of population growth the most important factor was the widespread adoption of better sanitation, the control of pestilence and plagues, and the consequent lowering of the death rate, including the reduction of infant mortality. These advances, in greater or less degree, affected every country, whether in Europe, the New World or the Orient. In the short span of four generations, or a hundred years, the world's population almost doubled and as the twentieth century opened stood at approximately 1,600,-000,000.

Since the year 1900 this extraordinary upward surge in the numbers of people has continued. Another 800,-000,000, in round numbers, have been added to the world population within the last fifty years, bringing us up to a present population of about 2,400,000,000. By the end of the present century, if the same rates of increase continue, and barring the cataclysm of atomic war, the total world population will stand at 3,600,000,000.

There are various ways by which one can attempt to visualize the significance of this almost incredible population growth. For instance, the present rate of increase results, each year, in approximately thirty million additional people — a number equal to the population of almost four cities the size of London or New York, or to put it another way, of six cities the size of Paris or Tokyo. Perhaps a more vivid comparison is that the net increase since the year 1900, namely, some eight hundred million people, exceeds the sum total of the populations of Europe, North and South America and Africa in that year. No wonder we are witness to a succession of violent and mounting pressures upon the social and political institutions of our times.

A few general observations should be made here regarding the distribution of population as well as regarding population increase. It is well to bear in mind that throughout historical times, as is the case today, at least half of all the world's people have lived in Asia. Consequently, the greatest pressures of people appear to be there. Further, in view of the fact that a number of Asiatic countries contain the largest populations of any of the world's regions, they have produced the largest numerical increase. This fact has given rise to the misconception that the rate of increase in Far Eastern countries is greater than in countries in other parts of the world. This is not true. For example, the rate of increase in Europe since the year

1800 is considerably greater than that in India during the same period. This surprising circumstance is principally due to the steady decline in the death rate in Europe during this period. Further, there are a number of instances of countries or regions — in the Americas, in Africa, or even a few in Europe — where the present rate of increase is either as great as, or in some cases greater than, that of India or other countries in the Far East.

On the other hand, there is a distinct tendency, which must not go unrecognized, for the rate of population growth to diminish in countries whose people have attained the advantages, both material and cultural, provided by modern civilization. A majority of the people in the world today, however, are living without these advantages. Consequently, it is not really sufficiently accurate to speak of a world population problem if, in doing so, one disregards the fact that the elements involved in the problem vary greatly in different countries or areas. Attempts are made from time to time to classify the people of the world into different categories designed to indicate differences in population patterns and food supply. For example, one authority has recently published a study that divides the countries of the world into the following three groups or areas.

The first consists of most of Western Europe, of North America, and of Australia and New Zealand.

This group contains about one fifth of the world's population and is characterized as having low birth rates, low death rates, high average food supply (estimated at three thousand calories per day) and a relatively stable population.

The second group, containing another one fifth of the world's population, consists of Eastern and Southeastern Europe, Spain, a few South American countries like Brazil and Argentina, and finally Japan. This group is described as having a moderate and rising industrial activity, a high but falling birth rate and a medium but falling death rate. These areas have the highest rates of natural increase largely because their birth rate has not been falling as fast as their death rate. They have a food level of between 2300 to 2800 calories per day — and so are living in a marginal state where countless individuals are underfed or suffering actual privation.

The third group is described as the truly critical one — and rightly so. It contains three fifths of the world's population and takes in most of Asia and some of its adjacent islands, most of Africa as well as major portions of South and Central America. Its population of almost one and a half billion people lives at or near a starvation level, with an estimated two thousand calories or less per day for each individual. It has a high and constant birth rate, a high but widely fluctuating death rate, which drops when harvests are good and there are no epidemics, and soars under opposite conditions. It represents a majority of the human race, innumerable people, living in a crisis whose monotone is interrupted only by catastrophe.

A grouping of the world's peoples, such as the above, which high-lights the differences in population and food conditions, is certainly invaluable in providing a clearer comprehension of the situation which faces humanity. However, as in all summaries that contain generalized statements, there is great risk of misunderstanding. For instance, the first group, which includes the countries in Western Europe and North America, is characterized as having "low birth rates . . . and a relatively stable population." Although this is generally true, two startling exceptions come to mind at once — and there are others. For instance, at this very time, the rates of net annual increase in the populations of both Holland and the United States are greater than the rate of India! As a matter of fact the birth rate in the United States in the year 1952 was unexpectedly high — climbing to 25 per thousand of population from a low of 16.6 per thousand in 1933. Both presumably represent temporary conditions, but the rise is illustrative of the fluctuations that may occur.

Considerable differences exist between both the birth and death rates of countries within any of the groups that have been described above. As we all know, almost every people or country possesses at least some individual characteristic, whether political, social, religious or economic. In the main, therefore, each country must find its own way through the dilemma created by population growth and resource inadequacy. And yet co-operative study and action can lead to practices that can prove invaluable to all.

A theory that the birth rate is highest among the ill-fed, and more particularly among those who lack protein in their diet, is not supportable as a uniform biological principle for mankind. There exists an overwhelming mass of evidence which confirms the self-evident fact that well-nourished people have the highest fertility potential and which also endorses the all-important truth that birth rate is primarily a consequence of economic and cultural influences.

It is sometimes said that one method of checking population increase is to provide an adequate diet and raise standards of living. There are scarcely any grounds for the belief that such a plan, even if it were possible to put it generally into effect, would produce the results that are constantly becoming more imperative. We have just seen that some high-living-standard countries, including even such countries as Holland and the United States, are capable of having a rapid rate of population increase. Further than that, even if it were possible to provide far more adequate diets to the hundreds of millions of presently undernourished people, the great likelihood is that the consequence would solely be more and more people. The infinitely tragic fact is that starvation is at present the only controlling factor to constantly increasing human numbers in a vast portion of our world. There are those who believe that this must always be so. They discredit the intelligence of mankind and disavow the possibilities that exist for the future of civilization. We do not live to extenuate the miseries of the past nor to accept as incurable those of the present.

There are stirrings within the minds of men — awakenings to what can and to what must be done. Already one great country in the Far East, India, is initiating a program to control population growth. Other peoples and countries are becoming more and more conscious of the nature of the dilemma. Sweden has adopted a program, unique of its kind, aimed at attaining a population improved as to quality and not diminishing in quantity. A world meeting on the subject of population, under the auspices of the United Nations, is now in prospect. Even though it is planned that this conference shall be statistical and technical in character, and free of what might be called social or political programing, it should prove yet one more step forward to understanding. The foundation of hope for the future lies in such understanding, all in good time transmitted through the processes of enlightenment and education to peoples of all countries. Such forward steps represent an attainable alternate to the creed of the pessimist, who holds that our civilization is incapable of delivering itself from a problem of this character and magnitude.

The rapid and continuing growth in world population is not necessarily due to increase in the birth rate. In the main it is due to the decline in the death rate. This decline is, of course, a direct consequence of advances in medical science, of widespread adoption of better sanitation and other public-health measures. The successes that have been gained so far in the conquest of epidemics and disease and in the alleviation of bodily pain and suffering represent, probably, the most beneficent accomplishment of modern times. The continuance and further development of public-health measures, as an essential part of humanitarianism, is infinitely desirable. At the same time it would be a gross delusion if it were not clearly recognized that such measures represent a potent, manmade control over natural forces that keep population in check.

This latter fact lies at the heart of a rational consideration concerning the desirability of using direct and effective means to control population growth. It lies at the crux of the argument as to whether birth control is good or undesirable. The situation is simply this. Modern man has gained the immeasurable benefits that have resulted from the advancement of medical science, whose techniques have largely removed the control of human numbers resulting from epidemics, plagues and disease. It must not be supposed that epidemics or pathological conditions are abnormal in nature. Wild animal populations are subject to them, and epidemics are one controlling factor upon population growth, although it seems that a principal one is lack of food supply. In effect, then, medical science through "unnatural methods" has at one and the same time ameliorated suffering and vastly increased human numbers. It is an irony of life that this great good should also bring this great problem in its train. The question remains. If we are to accept, as of course we must, the continuing and ever-greater boon that public health measures afford humanity, must we not take adequate steps to abolish the disastrous consequences of overpopulation, to which medical science is an unintentional contributor?

One of the principal impediments to an objective approach to birth control stems from religious dogma. This has been true during much of the past just as it is today. Beliefs concerning the inviolability of the human soul and ethical conceptions of the rights and wrongs of human action have greatly affected human thinking as to whether man is justified in interfering with natural procreation. Gandhi, India's great spiritual leader and ascetic, held that abstinence from intercourse was the desirable and indeed the only method that should be used to keep population in check. It is noteworthy that many of his followers, now become leaders in India, have grown to realize that relief from their country's population crisis cannot be gained if reliance is placed upon abstinence alone and, consequently, that the adoption of other and more realistic approaches is imperative.

In the Western world the attitude of the Catholic church is, at the present time, a strong influence in discouraging open discussion and preventing a completely detached approach to a problem which is of such overriding importance to the future welfare and happiness of mankind. Speaking as a Protestant, I think it unjustified, indeed wrong, that those of other faiths should attack the Catholic attitude with a violence that is all too frequent. The answer to the present common emergency will be too long delayed if the search for it is clouded by bitterness or misunderstanding.

It can never be amiss to recall that the Catholic church is one of the foremost defenders of the free world against the evils of communism and at the same time a bulwark in modern society against the dissolution of the family as a social unit. Both of these significant accomplishments, however, create a paradox. Communism flourishes best amidst conditions of need or want, and such conditions are unquestionably fostered by the pressures of ever-increasing numbers of people upon limited resources. In contrast, the welfare of the family is diminished when standards of living inevitably decline in the face of overpopulation. This is the hour when different faiths and creeds can well join together in the attempt to resolve a paradox that is common to all.

Time presses on. Every twenty-four hours there are seventy-five thousand or more additional people on the earth.

How will the ever-increasing needs of our world's constantly larger population be met? It is clear from the considerations in earlier pages that the returns being gained from agriculture in the cultivated regions of the earth are barely able to meet existing demands — and in many instances failing to. It is also evident that the potentialities of such regions as the Amazon or parts of Africa offer no early or even assured solution. Further, it is apparent from the appraisals made in the preceding chapter that present knowledge of practical means to draw upon the life resources of the oceans of the world, or to create artificial subsistence, or to convert salt water to fresh for important extensions of agricultural lands is in each and every case in an incipient stage. Perhaps one day these new resources, or new methods of providing essential resources, may be of importance, but that day, at best, is a long way off.

It is said quite often — particularly by specialists who are themselves responsible for the invaluable advances being made in agricultural techniques — that if existing knowledge could be universally applied the problem would be resolved. There is no way of disputing such a statement, and, therefore, no purpose can be gained in trying to deny it. However, the statement bears resemblance to one that might be made to the effect that if everyone would act just as he should there would be no need for law courts, police officers or even standing armies.

The effort towards a far more extensive adoption of sound and competent agricultural methods is indeed essential — nor, as it happens, is such an effort unrelated to the realization of higher ethical standards. As a case in point, the land-tenure systems that still prevail in many countries are not only inefficient but inequitable. Recent land revolutions in India, the Near East, Italy and elsewhere are a sign of the times, though, it must be recognized, they have occurred frequently before in history. The Russians are committed to seeking the solution through the establishment of collective farms, where all lands belong to the state. The aim of the free world is the encouragement of individual ownership and responsibility — a system that not only answers the desire for freedom of action but, competitively, holds greater promise of results. It is questionable whether, regardless of the "urge" from the state, any collective Soviet farm could match the extraordinary and long-sustained results produced, for example, by the land-holding farmers of northern Europe, or by farming communities such as those of the Amish and the Mennonites in the United States, where land and individual welfare, present and future, are one.

More equitable land-tenure systems are obviously an important requirement in the development of world agriculture. Even with all the faith one must hold in the future, these changes for the better can, at best, be accomplished only gradually. Better land use, not unlike better morals, is hard to attain.

The prospects for a substantial increase in agricultural production must be measured, in large part, in the light of past accomplishments as well as of existing conditions. As to the former, the recent report of the United Nations Food and Agricultural Organization is so significant that it cannot be disregarded. It will be recalled that this survey states that the increase in world food supply, during somewhat more than the last decade, has failed to keep pace with population growth — food supply having increased by 9 per cent and population by 12 per cent. This failure has occurred despite all the current efforts to close the gap. As to existing conditions, one need only recall the present situation in Europe, the weakening of the position of the food-surplus countries, the impediments that lie ahead in the undeveloped regions, such as Africa or the Amazon, to realize the magnitude of the task in the face of known realities.

It is to be expected that there can be no general

agreement as to the prospective rate of increase in world food production — any more than there can be a commonly shared opinion concerning any future event. Some maintain that the blight of soil erosion, so prevalent, and even accelerating, in many countries, will offset the advances that are being made in technical knowledge and that consequently we shall be fortunate if the present rates of production are maintained. Others — and especially those who, as professionals, are intimately aware of the recently discovered values of better crop species, such as hybrid corn, or are themselves making discoveries in the science of soil chemistry — envisage immeasurable results if these new knowledges could be generally applied. Still others suggest that there must be extensive regions on the earth that are not now being used, though failing to define where these regions may be or to analyze their presumed potentialities. Finally, others claim that we can fill our needs from the oceans, or create synthetic substitutes, or that the genii of technology, when they really put their minds to the task, will find the answers to the question for which humanity is now waiting. It is profoundly hoped that this book will throw the light of realism on these urgent questions and, among other things, will dispel illusions regarding imaginary new horizons.

A settlement of existing differences of opinion is obviously most difficult. All must be tempered by two overriding considerations. The first is the condition of man himself, or, specifically, the cultural, economic, and even political circumstances which govern his actions. The second is the natural environment or, specifically, the conditions of climate, land form, soil, vegetation and water supply which are favorable or otherwise to human existence. The endeavor in preceding chapters has been to provide illustrations of the potency of these influences.

Out of the welter of conflicting opinions and bold, if not careless, forecasts, only one valid or practical observation can be made. It will be time to conjecture how many people the earth is capable of supporting when the increase in the production of vital resources from agriculture, or through other means, is demonstrably keeping pace with population growth. This it is not now doing.

It is a rather curious contemporary circumstance, when well-founded opinions are of the essence, that some scientists are playing the role of prophets of abundance. In entering the realm of conjecture, they are abandoning the so-called "scientific method," which demands conclusions based on known facts and conditions. Theirs is a heavy and unenviable responsibility if, as time runs on, their anticipations are proved groundless and public opinion has been grossly misled. A recent headline in a newspaper with an international circulation ran, WORLD HELD ABLE TO FEED 4

BILLION. Within the last few years there have been a number of similar widely quoted statements from "authoritative sources." One's first reaction might well be that the world is not now successful in feeding half that number. In justice to the authors of such statements, they almost invariably cover their positions with the proviso which runs, "If present knowledges could be efficiently applied throughout the world." This, of course, is the crux of the matter. The barrier is not so much lack of knowledge as that imposed by conditions, cultural, and economic, that govern men's actions. These conditions are the existing verities that no one, scientist or otherwise, is justified in disregarding.

Quite apart from food supply, there is the other question as to the adequacy of the earth's stores of minerals, chemicals and petroleum, as well as other energy producers, to meet the expanding demands of our industrial civilization. These other natural resources, spoken of as "nonrenewable," are finite, so that one day many of them will be exhausted. The mounting tempo in the use of the nonrenewable resources, referred to briefly in the earlier chapter on the United States, is exemplified by the statement quoted there to the effect that the quantity of most metals and mineral fuels used in the United States in the last forty years exceeds the total used throughout the entire world in all preceding history. A consideration of the implication

224

of facts such as these is not within the purpose of this book. Nevertheless, it is evident that, year by year, the entire problem of adequacy of natural resources for the maintenance and development of our civilization is becoming more acute. There is no doubt that science and technology face their greatest opportunities in the discovery of new inorganic resources or in the replacement of one diminishing raw material by another of which there are larger reserves. Presumably, there are within the earth large quantities of non-renewable resources that have not as yet been discovered and put to use. These and similar technological expectancies will not, however, answer the primal question of food supply and other organic resources needed to support life as well as a substantial part of the world's industry.

The discovery of nuclear energy marks an epoch in the history of man. On the other hand, it becomes a meaningless incident if we do not intelligently conserve, use and develop the life-supporting elements of the earth — its soils, forests and water resources — and at the same time measure the numbers of people who can be supported by the productivity of the earth. Impressive beyond comprehension are the technological advances of this era. The stark fact remains — nuclear energy means nothing to the man whose body is starving.

Some people who are wedded to the magical idea

of limitless technological development may say, "Give us time. The day may come when even nuclear energy, in some manner, can be employed as an agent to provide for the needs of innumerable people." Even if we care to envision such a fantasy becoming a reality, we still must ask ourselves, "Is the purpose of our civilization really to see how much the earth and the human spirit can sustain?" The decision is still ours to make, assuming we recognize that the goal of humanitarianism is not the quantity but the quality of living.

If we evade the choice, the inevitable looms ahead of us — even sterner forces will make the decision for us. We cannot delay or evade. For now, as we look, we can see the limits of the earth.

ACKNOWLEDGMENTS

It is not easy, if indeed possible, to make a sufficient expression of gratitude to those who aid in the writing of a book such as this. A number have given invaluable assistance in gathering facts and material, others have been extremely helpful with suggestions and criticisms. My appreciation to all cannot be adequately put into words.

My warm thanks go to the following who have gathered or prepared reference material, or, in turn, given valuable suggestions as to sources of information: Alden Stevens, Gösta Netzen, Philip Wolf, Robert West Howard, George J. Stolnitz, Harding le Riche, Simon J. Ellison, and the late Sir Keith Murdoch of Australia. The writings of Robert C. Cook, editor of the *Population Reference Bureau,* which have appeared in that publication, have proved of much value.

Lionel A. Walford drew upon his rich experience and knowledge for the preparation of the study of marine resources. Herbert Bronstein gathered together and prepared the material which comprises the chapter on South Africa. Special thanks go to Edward C.

Higbee. Because of his own field experience in the Amazon, combined with his technical knowledge of agronomy and related subjects, he made invaluable contributions to the chapter on that great region and in addition was largely responsible for the material on Africa.

Then there were those who were good enough to give generously of their time in reading certain parts of the book containing subject matter with which they were especially familiar: For this help I am grateful to Felisberto Cardoso de Camargo, John A. Logan and Courtland B. Manifold for their review of the chapter on the Amazon; to Robert P. Messenger for his review of the material on Australia; to R. J. Harrison-Church of London and George H. T. Kimble for their constructive criticisms of the chapter on Africa. Kingsley Davis has been helpful in a number of ways, including his review and criticisms of the chapters on Africa and the Far East. Pascal K. Whelpton was kind enough to advise regarding population data in the final chapter.

The two organizations with which I am associated — the Conservation Foundation and the New York Zoological Society — aided greatly in making possible the considerable amount of research work that was necessary. At the same time my associates in both organizations were generous in help and in encouragement. Peter M. Stern of the staff of the Conservation Foundation assisted capably in checking data and material. When the manuscript was completed, George E. Brewer gave invaluable advice as to the rearrangement of text, which led to improved sequences in some of the chapters as well as to better emphasis on some of the principal ideas this book endeavors to express.

Finally, I am indebted to Rosalie E. Sevcik, assisted by E. Loretto Hoey, for painstaking care in the preparation of the manuscript and in the compilation of reference material.

While those mentioned above have greatly helped in making this book as factually correct as possible, they should not be held responsible for any statements, implications, theories or opinions that are found in these pages.

F. O.

BIBLIOGRAPHY AND READING LIST

CHAPTER I

Botsford, George Willis, *A History of Rome*. The Macmillan Company, New York, 1901.

Chapman, Charles E., *A History of Spain*. The Macmillan Company, New York, 1944.

Echeverría, Leonardo, Martín, *España: El País y los Habitantes*. Editorial Atlante, S. A., Mexico, D.F., 1940.

Ferlet, Jules, *Population Problems of the Time of Augustus*. Eugenics Research Association, Monograph No. 7, Cold Spring Harbor, New York, 1933.

Gavira, José, *España: La Tierra, El Hombre, El Arte*. Tomo I, Editorial Alberto Martín, Barcelona, 1943.

Simkhovitch, Vladimir G., "Rome's Fall Reconsidered." *Political Science Quarterly,* Vol. XXXI, June 1916, pp. 201–243.

Thompson, James W., *An Economic and Social History of the Middle Ages, 300–1300*. Century Company, New York, 1928.

Toynbee, Arnold J., *A Study of History*. Oxford University Press, New York, 1947.

Toynbee, Arnold J., *Greek Historical Thought* (From Homer to the Age of Heraclius). J. M. Dent, London, 1924.

CHAPTER II

Notestein, Frank W., and others, *The Future Population of Europe and the Soviet Union*. League of Nations, Geneva, Switzerland, 1944.

Cook, Robert C., "Europe's Overpopulation." Population Reference Bureau, *Population Bulletin,* Vol. VIII, No. 1, Feb. 1952.

Trevelyan, G. M., *Illustrated English Social History*. Longmans, Green & Company, Inc., New York, 1942.

United Nations Department of Social Affairs, Population Division, *Population Bulletin,* No. 1, Dec. 1951.

United States Department of State, *Point 4—What It Is and How It Operates*. Technical Co-operation Administration, July 1951.

Von Hofsten, Nils, "Sterilization in Sweden." *Journal of Heredity,* Vol. XL, No. 9, Sept. 1949.

CHAPTER III

Clark, Colin, "Australian Over-Industrialisation." *Manchester Guardian Weekly,* Vol. LXVI, No. 11, March 13, 1952, p. 12.

Food and Agriculture Organization of the United Nations, *Second World Food Survey*. Rome, Nov. 1952.

McConkey, O. M., *Conservation in Canada*. J. M. Dent & Sons, Ltd., Toronto, Canada, 1952.

United Nations Department of Economic Affairs, *Economic Survey of Latin America*. New York, 1951.

CHAPTER IV

Colm, Gerhard, *The American Economy in 1960*. National Planning Association, Washington, D.C., Planning Pamphlets, No. 18, Dec. 1952.

Davis, Joseph S., *Our Changed Population Outlook and Its Significance*. Stanford University Press, Stanford, California, 1951.

Forbes, W. H., "What Will India Eat Tomorrow?" *The Atlantic Monthly,* Vol. CLXXXVIII, Aug. 1951, pp. 36–40.

Hartley, Sir Harold, "Agriculture as a Potential Source of Raw Materials for Industry." *Journal of the Textile Institute,* Vol. XXVIII, No. 7, July 1937.

Paley, William S., *Resources for Freedom*. A Report to the President by the President's Materials Policy Commission. 5 Vols., Washington, June 1952.

Shaw, Byron T., *The Job Ahead for Agriculture*. Testimony before United States House Subcommittee on Agricultural Appropriations, Feb. 5, 1952. (In: *Hearings,* Part I, pp. 228–251.)

Thom, W. J., Jr., "Tectonic Team-Research. Key to Social Progress and World Peace." *Transactions of New York Academy of Sciences,* Vol. XIV, Feb. 1952, pp. 146–151.

Thomas, Harold E., *The Conservation of Ground Water*. McGraw-Hill Book Company, Inc., New York, 1951.

United States Department of Agriculture, Bureau of Agricultural Economics, *Agriculture's Capacity to Produce*. Agricultural Information Bulletin No. 88, June 1952.

Whitaker, J. Russell, and Ackerman, Edward A., *American Resources*. Harcourt, Brace & Company, Inc., New York, 1951.

CHAPTER V

Carr-Saunders, A. M., *World Population: Past Growth and Present Trends*. Clarendon Press, Oxford, 1937.

Pendleton, Robert L., "The Belgian Congo: Impressions of a Changing Region." *Geographical Review,* Vol. XXXIX, No. 3, July 1949, pp. 371–400.

Shantz, H. L., and Marbut, C. F., *The Vegetation and Soils of Africa*. American Geographical Society, New York, 1923.

Stamp, L. Dudley, *Africa*. John Wiley & Sons, Inc., New York, 1953.

Welsh, Anne E. (editor), *Africa South of the Sahara*. Oxford University Press, New York, 1951.

Wood, Alan, *The Groundnut Affair*. John Lane, The Bodley Head, Ltd., London, 1950.

CHAPTER VI

de Kiewiet, C. W., *A History of South Africa, Social and Economic*. Clarendon Press, Oxford, 1941.

Fosdick, R. B., *The Story of the Rockefeller Foundation*. Harper and Brothers,, New York, 1952.

James, Selwyn, *South of the Congo*. Random House, Inc., New York, 1943.

Ross, J. C., "Southward Moves the Desert." *Annual of South Africa,* 1949–1950.

CHAPTER VII

Bates, Marston, *Where Winter Never Comes*. Charles Scribner's Sons, New York, 1952.

James, Preston E., *Latin America*. Revised Edition, Odyssey Press, Inc., New York, 1950.

Le Cointe, Paul, *L'Amazonie Brésilienne*. 3 Vols., Paris, Belém, 1922–1934.

Marbut, C. F., and Manifold, C. B., "The Topography of the Amazon Valley." *Geographical Review,* Vol. XV, 1925, pp. 617–642.

Netto, F. Ferreira, "The Problem of the Amazon." *Scientific Monthly,* Vol. LXI, July 1945, pp. 33-44.

CHAPTER VIII

Cressey, George B., *Asia's Lands and Peoples.* Second Edition, McGraw-Hill Book Company, Inc., New York, 1951.

Davis, Kingsley, *The Population of India and Pakistan.* Princeton University Press, Princeton, New Jersey, 1951.

India, Government Planning Commission, *The First Five Year Plan, A Draft Outline.* New Delhi, July 1951.

Lorimer, Frank, *The Population of the Soviet Union: History and Prospects.* League of Nations, Geneva, Switzerland, 1946.

CHAPTER IX

Adams, Roger, "Man's Synthetic Future." *Science,* Vol. CXV, No. 2981, Feb. 15, 1952, pp. 157-163.

Alverson, D. L., "Deep-water Trawling Survey Off the Coast of Washington, Aug. 17-Oct. 19, 1951." *Commercial Fisheries Review,* Vol. XIII, No. 11, Nov. 1951, pp. 1-16.

Ayres, Eugene, and Scarlott, Charles A., *Energy Sources, The Wealth of the World.* McGraw-Hill Book Company, Inc., New York, 1952.

Brittain, Robert, *Let There Be Bread.* Simon & Schuster, Inc., New York, 1952.

Burchard, John Ely (editor), *Mid-Century; The Social Implications of Scientific Progress.* The Technology Press of Massachusetts Institute of Technology, Cambridge, Massachusetts, and John Wiley & Sons, Inc., New York, 1950.

Burlew, John S. (editor), *Algal Culture: From Laboratory to Pilot Plant*. Publication No. 600, Carnegie Institution of Washington, D.C., July 1953.

Ellson, J. G., Powell, Donald E., and Hildebrand, Henry H., *Exploratory Fishing Expedition to the Northern Bering Sea in June and July, 1949*. Fishery Leaflet 369, United States Department of the Interior, Fish and Wildlife Service, 1950.

Shropshire, R. F., "Plankton Harvesting." *Journal of Marine Research,* Vol. V, 1944, pp. 185-188.

United Nations Scientific Conference on the Conservation and Utilization of Resources, *Proceedings,* Vol. VII: *Wildlife and Fish Resources*. United Nations Department of Economic Affairs, New York, 1951.

Warfel, Herbert E., and Manacop, P. R., *Otter Trawl Explorations in Philippine Waters*. Research Report No. 25, United States Department of the Interior, Fish and Wildlife Service, 1950.

Wigutoff, Norman B., and Carlson, Clarence J., *A Survey of the Commercial Fishery Possibilities of Seward Peninsula Area, Kotzebue Sound, and Certain Inland Rivers and Lakes in Alaska*. Fishery Leaflet 375, United States Department of the Interior, Fish and Wildlife Service, 1950.

CHAPTER X

Thompson, Warren S., "Population." *Scientific American,* Vol. CLXXXII, No. 2, Feb. 1950, pp. 11-15.

GENERAL

Bennett, Merrill K., "Population, Food, and Economic Progress." *The Rice Institute Pamphlet,* Vol. XXXIX, No. 2, July 1952.

Black, John D., and Kiefer, Maxine E., *Future Food and Agriculture Policy*. McGraw-Hill Book Company, Inc., New York, 1948.

Brittain, Robert, *Let There Be Bread*. Simon & Schuster, New York, 1952.

Clark, Colin, *The Conditions of Economic Progress*. Revised edition, Macmillan & Company, Ltd., London, 1951.

Clark, F. Le Gros, and Pirie, N. W. (editors), *Four Thousand Million Mouths*. Oxford University Press, New York, 1951.

Cook, Robert C., *Human Fertility: The Modern Dilemma*. William Sloane, Associates, Inc., New York, 1951.

Davis, Kingsley (editor), "World Population in Transition." *Annals of the American Academy of Political and Social Science,* Vol. CCXXXVII, Jan. 1945, especially "The World Demographic Transition," pp. 1–11.

DeTurk, E. E. (editor), "Freedom from Want." *Chronica Botanica,* Vol. XI, No. 4, Summer 1948.

Food and Agriculture Organization of the United Nations, *The State of Food and Agriculture, Review and Outlook*. Rome, 1952.

Gill, Tom, *Land Hunger in Mexico*. Charles Lathrop Pack Forestry Foundation, Washington, D.C., 1951.

Hartley, Sir Harold, "Limiting Factors in World Development: What Is Possible?" *Annual Proceedings of the Associated Scientific and Technical Societies of South Africa, 1947–1948,* Johannesburg, 1949.

Hatt, Paul (editor), *World Population and Future Resources*. *Proceedings,* 2nd Centennial Academic Conference of Northwestern University, 1951. American Book Company, New York, 1952.

Linton, Ralph (editor), *Most of the World; The Peoples*

of Africa, Latin America, and the East Today. Columbia University Press, New York, 1949.

Our Imperiled Resources. 17th Annual Forum, New York Herald Tribune, New York, 1948.

"Problems of Development of Densely Settled Areas and Scientific Possibilities for Increasing the World's Food Supply." American Philosophical Society, *Proceedings,* Vol. XCV, No. 1, Feb. 13, 1951, pp. 1–54.

Roberts, Michael, *The Estate of Man*. Faber & Faber, Ltd., London, 1951.

Stamp, L. Dudley, *Land for Tomorrow, The Underdeveloped World*. Indiana University Press, Bloomington, Indiana, 1952.

United Nations Scientific Conference on the Conservation and Utilization of Resources, *Proceedings,* Vols. I–VIII, Aug.–Sept., 1949, Department of Economic Affairs, New York, 1951.

Zimmermann, Erich W., *World Resources and Industries*. Second Edition, Harper & Brothers, New York, 1951.